SWORD STUDY
NOTEBOOK

Senior Edition

Written by
Tammy McMahan

Illustrations by
Doug McGuire

Vignettes by
Marti Pieper

Sword Study Notebook
Senior Edition

2012 SWORD STUDY NOTEBOOK, Senior Edition
Copyright © 2012 The Shelby Kennedy Foundation
Published by Glass Road Media
First printing February 2013

ISBN: 978-0-9884789-3-0

Dewey Decimal Classification Number: 227

Scripture quotations identified KJV are taken from the King James Version.

Scripture quotations identified NKJV are taken from the New King James Version. Copyright © 1982 by Thomas Nelson, Inc. Used by permission. All rights reserved.

Scripture quotations identified NASB are taken from the The Holy Bible, NEW AMERICAN STANDARD VERSION. Copyright © 1960, 1962, 1968, 1971, 1972, 1973, 1975, 1977, 1995 by The Lockman Foundation. Used by permission. All rights reserved.

Scripture quotations identified NIV are taken from the HOLY BIBLE, NEW INTERNATIONAL VERSION. Copyright © 1973, 1978, 1984 by the International Bible Society. Used by permission of International Bible Society. All rights reserved.

Scripture quotations identified ESV are taken from The English Standard Version. Copyright © 1993, 1994, 1995, 1996, 2000, 2001, 2002. Used by permission, Crossway Division of Good News Publishers. All rights reserved.

Word Study Part A entries based on Strong's Exhaustive Concordance of the Bible and Greek Dictionary of the New Testament. Word Study Part B entries are based on Vine's Concise Dictionary of the Bible, and Zodhiate's Complete Word Study Dictionary: New Testament.

Printed in the United States of America.

For more information about resources for studying the Bible together as a family, or to order additional copies of this resource, visit www.biblebee.org.

Glass Road Media and Management
www.glassroadmm.com

SWORD STUDY
NOTEBOOK

NAME

PHONE

START DATE

COMPLETION DATE

DEDICATION

To the glory and honor of
my Heavenly Father

To my sons, Alex, Zachary and Hunter:
Seek Him!
Continue in the spirit of power,
love and discipline.

ACKNOWLEDGEMENTS

Many thanks, continued prayers day & night and love to . . .

. . . Mark, the perfect husband for me;
you are my faithful, supportive and protecting provision from the Lord. Thee I love.

. . . Alex, Zachary, Hunter, Ashley and Abigail, dearest Timothy's, I love you so much!
*My greatest prayer is that you would know your Lord through His Word
so that you would love Him passionately and live for Him wholly.*

. . . Barb Widdoes, my Eunice and Paul;
*you are my faithful friend, example of servanthood and an unashamed,
approved workman of the Word. You are a gift of gifts from the Lord to me.*

. . . Tom Widdoes, my Paul;
*you are my rock-solid, joyful, wisdom-giving, wise father.
You are the best example of our Heavenly Father for me.*

. . . Jill Dant, my dear Barnabus-like friend;
you are a sweet encourager, dear cohort and the best editor ever.

. . . Caroline McKenzie, my dear daughter in Christ;
you are a sweet, diligent Timothy indeed!

. . . Kristy West, my dear fellow sojourner;
your Spirit-led notes and gifts are a great joy to my spirit.

. . . Marti Pieper, my dear friend in pink;
your Spirit-led prayers and support from stages to stories are a blessing beyond words.

. . . Twila and Ken, our dear family;
*your partnership in the walk of training, supporting and building
is a constant encouragement to Mark and me.*

. . . Mary Kathryn and Tracy, our dear family;
*your battling prayers and coming alongside in the work and love
are such great examples of Christ's love to me and our family.*

. . . Susan Carter, my dear fellow friend in the Word;
your diligence in the walk of righteousness and support are a constant encouragement.

. . . Amy and Frank, our dear family;
*your fun-loving, joyful presence in my life and my family's lives is a cause for grateful praise
for the encouragement and sweet fellowship.*

. . . Eastlyn, Steve, Bill and Rich, the small but mighty Foundation team;
you are a tremendous example of serving the Lord in word and deed. It is a joy to work alongside you.

***. . . Linda, Ginny, Carol, Kellie, Cheri, Steph, Dawn, Julie, Jen,
Gina, Dana, Doreen, Jennifer and Cheryl, my faithful,
enduring prayer warriors and friends from near and far;***
*you are the Lord's gifts to me! Your notes, perfectly timed encouragement and friendships
are an invaluable gift from the Lord to me!*

***. . . Kelsey, Kristen, Susan, Tom, Kristi, Caroline, Barb and
Jill, my enduring, diligent review team;***
you are greatly appreciated for your faithful, diligent work.

Thank you!

5

ENDORSEMENTS

"The Sword Studies are a great tool to help parents who desire to raise kids who whole-heartedly love the Lord.   They meet each family member right where they're at, and keep the parents in the role of mentor, teacher and model for their own children."
Kirk Cameron *Actor, Author*

"The Sword Studies uniquely offer appropriately-leveled, individual study on the same book of the Bible for each family member, which then builds a strong foundation of Scriptural knowledge and spiritual growth for the whole family. If more families would invest in systematic, in-depth Bible study and memorization like this, the end result may be a much-needed revival in our churches, communities and nation."
Nancy Leigh DeMoss *Author, Revive Our Hearts radio host*

"Your kids' Christian worldview won't hold up to the culture's bombardment if you build it with superficial materials. Teach them to dig into the meat of the Word of God for themselves, help them learn to feast on it and be so satisfied that the world pales in comparison. Sword Studies are an invitation to the feast, a logical investigation of one book of the Bible partnered with prayer, memorization and discipleship that will foster a solidly Christian paradigm in your children's hearts and minds."
Sean McDowell *Educator, Speaker, Author*

"I highly recommend the investigative method of studying the Bible- the Sword Studies do this from top to bottom for the whole family. Gather your family and soak up His life-giving truth with the help of this excellent tool!"
Joni Eareckson Tada *Founder, Chief Executive Officer, Joni and Friends International Disability Center*

"The family that takes on the daily discipline of this 'Sword Study' is setting itself up for the discovery of all kinds of unexpected blessings."
Joel Belz *Founder, World Magazine*

"As a Christian parent, you recognize the need to lead your children spiritually. But how do you do it? These age-specific Bible studies are just that tool. They can be completed individually, or as an entire family together. This is everything you need for serious family discipleship at home!"
Ryan Frank *Executive Director, KidzMatter, Vice President, Innovative Strategies, Awana*

WELCOME

God has important and very helpful truths for you in His Word.
As you spend time in His Word studying, observing, and meditating
– alone and together with your family – our prayer is that God will
deepen your knowledge of Him and His Word, build and strengthen
your relationship with Him, and equip you for the work that He has
set forth for you to do! Prepare and get ready for action!

This is what the LORD says:
"Let not the wise man boast of his wisdom or the
strong man boast of his strength or the rich man
boast of his riches, but let him who boasts boast
about this: that he understands and knows me, that
I am the LORD, who exercises kindness, justice
and righteousness on earth, for in these I delight,"
declares the LORD.

Jeremiah 9:23-24 (New International Version 1984)

WEEK AT GLANCE

Weekly

AN INTRODUCTORY STORY
The first day of each week will begin with a vignette. It is designed to be a prelude to the main themes that you will be studying during the week.

FIVE DAYS OF STUDY
You will be led through five days of study each week. Each book's chapter will be studied over a two-week period, starting with an overview of the chapter and then moving through the Investigative Study to a final "Day 10 Diagram" summary of the entire chapter at the end of the two-week period.

Daily

ON YOUR KNEES: PRAY, WRITE, READ
You will begin each day by praying for a quiet and focused heart. Then, you will write out verses to create your own copy of Scripture in the WRITE! tab and read through the book.

INVESTIGATIVE STUDY: 1-2-3
You will be led through simple steps in the Investigative Study.

APPLY!
At the closing of each day of study, you will apply what you have learned that day. Then, at the end of each two-week period, you will summarize and fully "Apply!" all you have studied for each chapter.

Continued on next page...

WEEK AT GLANCE

Daily

A.C.T.S. Prayer

Each day will conclude with a guided prayer time to help you think through the Scriptures you investigated in your study. Initially, we will pray through each step of the A.C.T.S. prayer model. After the first week you are encouraged to write personal prayers within the Sword Study .

A - Adoration
In Adoration we will worship God for who He is and what He has done. We will focus on His character, attributes, and/or deeds that we saw in His Word that day.

C - Confession
In our time of Confession we will focus on our sin. We will take God's Word, hold it up to our hearts and our lives to see where we miss the mark. You will be led to go before the Lord and confess.

T - Thanksgiving
As we go to the Lord in Thanksgiving, we will express our gratitude to God for who He is and what He has done. We will thank Him for what we have learned about Him that day and for what He has revealed to us in His Word.

S - Supplication
When we approach God in Supplication, we will bring those study-related prayer requests before His throne. Instead of focusing on our circumstances, we will focus on what we have learned in His Word that day and ask Him to help us apply those truths to our lives.

SWORD STUDY OVERVIEW

1 - THE AERIAL VIEW

From our knees, we will move into our Investigative Study of the Bible. Your study begins with the Aerial View, in which you will read the entire book several times to help you become familiar with the text. This will show you the "lay of the land," like a photo taken from an airplane or a satellite. By researching the author, historical context and original recipients of the book, you will set the stage for more accurate understanding of the text. You will create your own book title that describes the central theme of the book. Your AERIAL VIEW observations will help you build a solid and true foundation for all that you will learn in the upcoming weeks. The Aerial View will be covered in Week One as we investigate the author, recipient, and the historical context of the book.

2 - THE STREETVIEW

As we continue, we will explore the book from a Streetview perspective, going in for a closer look and focusing in on one chapter at a time. The Streetview involves several exercises. First, you will make general observations of the chapter, looking for exhortations, commands, topics, or lists. Then, you will interview the chapter. From these observations, you will choose a title for the chapter. This exercise will be like knocking on someone's door and asking them questions. You will literally be interviewing the chapter by asking who, what, when, where, why, and how questions. Finally, you will search the chapter for any key words. In addition, as part of the daily Investigative Study, you will read through the chapter being studied, making any new or revised observations of the chapter.

3 - UNDER THE RUG

Under the Rug is when we really dig deep to uncover any hidden details. In this step, we will be identifying specific key words and looking up the original Greek words and their meanings. We refer to this step as a "Word Study." We will also look up cross references for the key words. These are Scriptures in other parts of the Bible that will provide deeper understanding and context for the key word.

APPLY!

Apply! is where we put it all together – from all the different views – to find what God reveals to us through our study of His Word. This will happen at different levels, depending on where you are in the chapter and on what part of the Investigative Study process you are in. Until you finish the Under the Rug level, the *Apply!* step each day will pertain in a general way to what you studied that day. Then on the last day of each chapter, you will have an opportunity to summarize through the unique "Day 10 Diagram". Finally, you will be able to apply what you have studied to how you live.

STUDY OF 2 TIMOTHY
A 10 Week Discipleship Study

Written by
Tammy McMahan

Illustrations by
Doug McGuire

Vignettes by
Marti Pieper

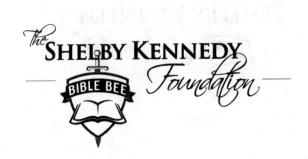

CONTENTS

SECTIONS

~ 1 ~

Overview

GETTING STARTED

~ 2 ~

1-2-3 APPLY!

SWORD STUDY

~ 3 ~

Write!

MY COPY OF 2 TIMOTHY

GETTING STARTED

FOCUS SCRIPTURES

"All Scripture is inspired by God and profitable for teaching, for reproof, for correction, for training in righteousness; so that the man of God may be adequate, equipped for every good work."

2 Timothy 3:16-17 New American Standard Bible

"Do you not know that those who run in a race all run, but only one receives the prize? Run in such a way that you may win. Everyone who competes in the games exercises self-control in all things. They then do it to receive a perishable wreath, but we an imperishable. Therefore I run in such a way, as not without aim; I box in such a way, as not beating the air; but I discipline my body and make it my slave, so that, after I have preached to others, I myself will not be disqualified."

1 Corinthians 9:24-27
New American Standard Bible

A LETTER
FROM THE APOSTLE PAUL

Dear Friends,

Thank you so much for the opportunity to continue the series of letters I began so long ago. When God gave me the words that became such a large part of the New Testament, I knew my legacy would extend beyond my lifetime. But I had no idea of the true impact it could have.

Did you know the Bible is the best-selling book in the world? Publishing records reveal it has sold more than six billion copies since its official publication in the 1400s. But of course Scripture was in existence long before that time. The power of God's Word has touched and changed countless lives. It truly is "living and active and sharper than any two-edged sword, and piercing as far as the division of joints and marrow, and able to judge the thoughts and intentions of the heart" (Hebrews 4:12).

In the letters I wrote to young churches, I often tried to teach. That's not too surprising since I spent the greatest part of my life after knowing Christ teaching and training others. You see, I had mentors in my own life. As a young Jewish boy, I trained in the school of Gamaliel, one of the most respected rabbis of our day. And after my conversion (turning around) on the road to Damascus, I needed a new kind of mentoring. First, the Holy Spirit taught me as I spent three years in the desert preparing for my new life and work. So I can speak from experience when I say there's no better teacher.

Once I returned from the desert, God placed a man in my life who served as my mentor, teacher, encourager, and friend. Barnabas ("son of encouragement") guided me by spending time with me.

We walked and talked together as we traveled to various churches, ministered, and eventually went on a mission trip together. Yes, we had a disagreement or two, but I will always honor and respect him as my true friend and mentor.

It comes as no surprise, then, that I sought to teach and encourage others through my writing as well as through my personal presence. God gave my ministry a broad reach, so I knew far more people than I could hope to revisit. I didn't have the many opportunities and means you have of staying in touch today, but I wrote my letters with a view to teach, train, and encourage believers as well as continuing to proclaim the gospel of Christ.

Sometimes I wrote words of warning. Sometimes I gave counsel. And always, I sought to show those who read my words the depth, length, height and breadth of the love of Christ.

I want you to know how proud I am that you are beginning this Sword Study. I find it an effective tool to help you not only to read and memorize God's Word (both of which are important), but to allow the Word to do its good work in you.

When God changed my life on that long-ago road, He accomplished something amazing. And as you learn to read, study, and apply His Word through this study, you'll watch as He does something amazing in you as well.

God has always worked through story. The Bible itself, as you know, is a story—not fiction or fantasy, but a true story of His work throughout history. Many of Scripture's teachings come through stories of long-ago people and the good, bad, wise, or unwise choices they made. And of course you know Jesus Christ himself loved to use story as a vehicle for communicating truth. When he spoke about a lost coin or scattered seed, he was telling stories intended to bring truth to his hearers in a fresh and understandable way.

As you work through the Sword Study this year, I want you to pay special attention to the story that accompanies each week. Your friends have chosen a series of heroes to teach, train, and encourage you in your walk with Christ. I know the stories of these nine different heroes and heroines will challenge and inspire you. Although we tell the stories in creative ways, the heroes are all real people and the lessons they teach will touch and change you.

Your life today may not look like anything these heroes describe. But as you read, I encourage you to ask the Holy Spirit to reveal points of intersection. He has something special to teach you through each one. And, in the same way Gamaliel and Barnabas mentored me, these hero-stories will mentor you, urging and equipping you to become the young adult Christ intends you to be.

Thank you again for allowing me to share my heart. I look forward to seeing you in heaven one day and hearing the hero-stories God gives you as you live your life for Him—

Grace be with you,

Paul

DAY ONE

ON MY KNEES:

Greetings! Are you excited to investigate 2 Timothy? Whether you are joining us for the first time or are a returning friend, our hope is that the format of this Sword Study will help to guide you in rightly dividing the Word of God. The method of allowing "Scripture to answer Scripture" will result in a deeper, more personal relationship between you and the Lord.

Each day before you begin an INVESTIGATIVE STUDY, the ON MY KNEES portion of your study will guide you through a time of focusing on the Lord through prayer and writing Scripture. Having a place and daily time set aside specifically to do your study will enable you to quiet your heart and focus on hearing from the Lord. Take a moment now to find a place that will allow you to meet with your Lord without distraction. All set?! Make sure your Bible and a pencil are next to you as you bow your head and heart in prayer to get started. Charge!

Pray. "I am here Lord; I am ready and want to hear from You as I begin my study of 2 Timothy. I am excited. I know this is a commitment. I am a little nervous, too. Give me the strength and perseverance to finish the course. Open my ears and eyes to Your ways. Help me to tune out the noise of my daily activities and tasks to focus on You and You alone. Amen."

Write. Since we will be looking at the book of 2 Timothy from an AERIAL VIEW this week, we will be writing passages that encourage us to know the Lord by studying His Word. On the lines below, write 2 Timothy 3:16-17*, which will also be one of our Focus Scriptures for 2 Timothy Sword Study. _____
_____
_____
_____
_____
_____

Read. Before you begin the INVESTIGATIVE STUDY portion of your Sword Study, we want you to hear directly from the Lord by reading Scripture. Your study's first week begins with an AERIAL VIEW, so you will be reading 2 Timothy in its entirety. This exercise will help give you familiarity and a solid foundation of the book. Do this all in one sitting and be purposeful in regulating your speed. Reading aloud can help to slow you down. Remember, this first time through, you are just going to familiarize yourself with the book.

INVESTIGATIVE STUDY
AERIAL

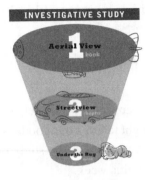

Apply!

We will spend these first few days looking at the whole text of 2 Timothy in order to gain a big-picture understanding of the book before we zoom in on the details. Now that you have read the book through once, answer the following questions. When applicable, be sure to note the reference of where you found your answer. Purpose to stay at cloud level during this time; trying to interpret any of the details at this point could sidetrack you.

What type of literature is 2 Timothy? _____

Who wrote 2 Timothy? _____

What were some of the difficulties he was experiencing?

_____

_____

From what location did he write 2 Timothy, according to verses 16 and 17 in Chapter 1?

_____

After reading 2 Timothy, what title would you give the book that would sum up its themes and message? Write down your initial thought here and continue to think about it throughout this week. Don't worry about figuring out the perfect title as you may end up with a completely different title after a more detailed investigation!   Title: _____

APPLY!

Who among your family and friends would be a good accountability partner? Think through those you know and choose someone whom you could ask to check in with you to see how you are doing with your daily time in the Sword Study. Ideally, it would be someone that you could help keep accountable to their own Sword Study! Give that person a call or write him or her an email. Ask this accountability partner to check in with you each week to ask what you have learned, and perhaps listen to one of your recommended Bible memory passages.

A.C.T.S. PRAYER TIME

Come before the Lord as you close your time in the Word. First, come to Him in **Adoration** of who He is. Next, share with Him where you know that you are falling short. **Confessing** the things that He brings to your attention allows for a clear conscience and an open relationship with Him. Follow with a time of gratitude, **Thanking** Him for all you have had been shown through the Scriptures and end with any **Supplications** that you have for Him in your living out what you have learned today.

A–"Lord, I want to lift Your name above all names. Thank You for giving me access to your grace, mercy and peace through Jesus Christ, my Savior."

C –"Lord, I know that I don't always depend on Your strength and I do what I feel like. Forgive me for putting myself above You."

T –"Thank you for gently correcting and lovingly encouraging me in my faith."

S –"Lord, give me the confidence and strength to stand firm in every area of my life. Help me see more of Your wonders within the pages of the Bible so that I might tell of Your goodness and sing praises to Your name. Help me to be diligent and meet You daily in the study of Your Word. Help me to do my Sword Study tomorrow and each day this week."

"The treasures of the Word of God are great beyond compare; but if we do not search them out, we cannot use what's there."
~Anonymous~

DIGGING DEEPER

Do you have a few extra moments to investigate? Paul called himself an Apostle. Go and find the general meaning of "apostle" and note what you find here:_____

_____

_____

_____

Since Timothy knew that Paul was an Apostle, why would Paul begin his letter with his title? Write your thoughts below:_____

_____

_____

_____

DAY TWO

ON MY KNEES:

Are you at your quiet meeting place with the Lord? Have you snuck away to that corner where you can sit at the Lord's feet undistracted? We will always begin with a prayer. We need the Holy Spirit's guidance as we study the Word of God. Today, we want to focus on thanking the Lord for His invitation to meet with Him. He is the One and only great God, the Creator of all things, but also our loving, heavenly Father who desires to dwell with us. Our recognition of these attributes of our God should drive us to our knees.

Pray. "Father, I want to give you the praise and honor that You deserve. How amazing to consider that You invite me into Your presence, not as an occasional visitor, but as an expected child. It is so easy for me to get caught up in the daily cares of my life and rush in and out of Your presence as just another task of the day. Give me a quiet, uninterrupted time with You as I bow my heart to study Your Word today. Teach me, refine me and strengthen me for Your purposes."

Write. Prayerfully write Psalm 36:10-11 in the lines below.

_____

_____

_____

_____

Read. Once again, remember that you are at the AERIAL VIEW getting the big picture of 2 Timothy. Committed reading before you begin your deeper investigation will help you create a solid foundation of learning. One of our objectives at this level is to get to know the author of the book. Keep an ear and eye out for any details about Paul as you read quietly to yourself.

INVESTIGATIVE STUDY
AERIAL

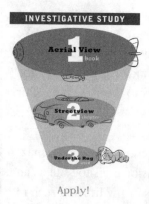

Apply!

Today, as you re-read 2 Timothy, did you notice all of the information that you learned about Paul? We are going to spend the day getting to know him. First, we will gather all that we can from our 2 Timothy passages. Then, we will look at what else we can glean from other areas of Scripture.

What was Paul's background? How did he come to the Lord? How did God use him to further the gospel? The answers to these questions will help us better understand the man God chose to speak to us through 2 Timothy. Did you know that Paul wrote 14 of the New Testament's 27 books? Let's get started on learning more about this great man of God.

What do you learn about Paul in the following 2 Timothy passages?

2 Timothy 1:1 _____

2 Timothy 1:3 _____

_____

2 Timothy 1:11 _____

2 Timothy 1:16-17 _____

2 Timothy 3:10-11 _____

_____

_____

2 Timothy 4:6 _____

2 Timothy 4:7-8 _____

_____

2 Timothy 4:16 _____

Titus 1:1-3* is another "greeting" by Paul. Investigate more of how Paul describes himself and what he proclaims in this verse, then go the extra mile and memorize the passage!

_____

_____

According to Philippians 3:4-8, what was Paul's background? _____

_____

_____

_____

Summarize Paul's conversion as described in Acts 9:1-20. _____

_____

What was Paul's birth name, according to Acts 13:9? _____

Where was Paul from? _____

What do we learn about Paul in Acts 22:24-29? _____

_____

Paul's walk on the road to Damascus dramatically changed the course of his life. Through his missionary travels and Spirit-inspired pen, he eventually altered the religious beliefs of the early first century. His godly devotion, leadership and example led to the creation of predominately-Gentile churches who worshiped the God of Israel, adhered to the Jewish moral code, but with less strict ritualistic obligations. Paul's faithful proclamation of the gospel of Jesus Christ and his teaching of a new covenant (or "new testament") helped establish the early church. He would become the Preacher of Preachers, and an apostle willing to die for His Savior. Second Timothy became his last will and testament. With death eminent, what would this great man of God cry out to his spiritual son and ultimately to us in the 21st century? May the Lord answer this question in an abundant way as we continue to study 2 Timothy over the next weeks!

APPLY!

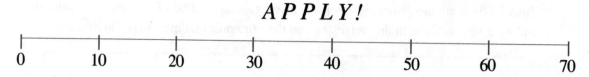

Research and complete a timeline of Paul's life and ministry. Make sure to include important events such as his birth, conversion and death. There are some differences of opinion among scholars, but general ranges of dates will be sufficient. You can investigate using your Logos software, Blue Letter Bible (http://www.blueletterbible.org/study/paul/timeline.cfm) or a Bible Dictionary.

A.C.T.S. PRAYER TIME

Open your Bible to Psalm 36:5-12 and read this short passage of praise. We are going to use it as the foundation of our closing prayer time with the Lord. During *Adoration*, praise the Lord for His lovingkindness to you. Take time to *Confess* any sins that may be hindering Your communion time with the Lord. Humble yourself before the Lord, for He loves the humble, but abhors the proud. Turn to *Thanksgiving* as you express your gratitude for being one of His children. Finish by asking *(Supplication)* Him for the desires of your heart according to His will.

A-"God of my forefathers, Your lovingkindness extends to the ends of the heavens and earth!"

C-"Lord, I confess that sometimes when I gain knowledge I feel prideful. Forgive me for thinking greater of myself than I should."

T-"God, thank You for providing for me abundantly and overflowing in every way I need. I am so blessed as Your child."

S-"Continue to show Your lovingkindness to me. I want to know You more. I want to have an upright heart that lives in righteousness. I know that this is only possible through Your strength and power. Help me to trust in You to work through me."

"The Bible is a supernatural book and can be understood only by supernatural aid."
~A.W. Tozer~

DIGGING DEEPER

In Acts, chapter 26, Paul is giving his defense against his imprisonment. Turn and read the chapter for a summary of Paul's life and beliefs. We will begin to see that regardless of the circumstances, Paul took every opportunity to proclaim what he believed, even if it was with his wrists and ankles bound in chains!

D A Y   T H R E E

ON MY KNEES:

How are you doing? The Lord is well pleased with your perseverance and dedication during these beginning days of your study. Sometimes these are the toughest days. Wrestling with reading the entire book repeatedly can be tiring. Our patience can be short, as we "just want to get to the point." Stand firm, my fellow student, because God promises that He will draw near to those who draw near to Him; even our earthly relationships are not built in just a few moments a day. Keep up the great work! As usual, begin your time on your knees.

Pray. "Jesus, my Lord, thank you for being my Savior! You gave up your will for the Father, so please help me to bow today before Your Word with a humble, willing heart. I want to learn more of how I can put my will aside and glorify You with my life. In Jesus' name, I pray. "

Write. Prayerfully and purposefully, write Psalm 119:73-74 on the lines below.

_____

_____

Read. Once again, please read 2 Timothy. As you read, watch for descriptions and details about the recipient or recipients of the letter.

INVESTIGATIVE STUDY
AERIAL

Apply!

The Scriptures were ultimately written to each and every one of us so that we might come to know, love and glorify the Lord of Heaven and Earth. Today, we are going to learn more about the direct recipient of 2 Timothy so we can understand how we are like him, and how Paul addressed his needs and strengths and encouraged him to grow in His relationship to Jesus Christ. We will begin by collecting what is hidden within 2 Timothy and then move to other areas of Scripture.

Who is the primary recipient of 2 Timothy according to Chapter 1, verse 2? _____

What do you learn about him in the following 2 Timothy, Chapter 1 verses?

Verse 2: _____

Verse 4: _____

What do you learn about Timothy in Acts 16:1-2? _____

How does Paul describe Timothy in 1 Corinthians 4:16-17?

_____

What evidence in this passage tells you that Paul trusts Timothy?

_____

What was Timothy's profession, according to 1 Timothy 4:13-16?

_____

According to Philippians 2:19-20, what was one of the ways Timothy assisted Paul?

_____

What do you learn of Timothy in 1 Thessalonians 3:2?

_____

Paul sends greetings to Priscilla, Aquilla and Onesiphorus in 2 Timothy because Timothy is with them. How did we find out where they were? Investigate these passages to find out more:

Acts 18:18-23 _____

1 Timothy 1:3 _____

In your own words, describe Timothy as if you were introducing him to a friend:

_____

_____

_____

_____

_____

APPLY!

Has God given you someone that encourages you in your walk with Christ? It has been said that we should have at least one Paul, one Timothy and one Barnabas in our lives. We are seeing this modeled before our eyes in much of the Scripture we have looked at today and especially in 2 Timothy. Consider these descriptions of the spiritual companions the Lord purposefully brings into our lives.

Our Barnabas can be of any age, but he or she encourages you in your faith and is willing to act as "iron sharpening iron" spiritually. Proverbs 17:17 is an excellent summary of this idea.
Our Timothy is usually a younger brother or sister in Christ that the Lord has brought into our lives for us to serve as an example, to encourage in the faith and lovingly challenge in his or her walk.

Finally, our Paul is one whom we can look up to in the faith. Often, this is our earthly father or mother as they disciple, encourage and live out the faith before our eyes. Many times, graciously, the Lord gives us other older men and women to come alongside us in our lives.

Take this time to think through who those people are in your life. While you are at it, consider who might be your Lois and Eunice, too!

List those names next to the Biblical names below.

Paul: _____

Timothy: _____

Barnabas: _____

Lois: _____

Eunice: _____

A.C.T.S. PRAYER TIME

As you have spent time evaluating and thinking of the different friends that the Lord has put in your life, let's turn our attention to the best friend we could ever have, Jesus Christ. His love, faithfulness and concern for our lives is unsurpassed. As we kneel for this time of prayer, begin with *Adoration* for His great, sacrificial love for you. *Confess* the times when He has not been your first love and you have put other people or things before Him. In *Thanksgiving*, thank Him for the people that He has uniquely and sovereignly placed in your life to help you grow closer to Him and His ways. Ask Him during *Supplication* for the insight and strength to be a Paul and Barnabus to others that He places in your life.

A-"Jesus, friend of mine, Your love and sacrifice are beyond my understanding. How great was Your love that You would give up Your throne and glorious dwelling to come save a sinner like me. There is no greater love. I have no greater friend than You."

C-"Lord, forgive me when I do not return Your love by putting You first in my life. Forgive me for choosing things and temporal activities over giving my life to you completely."

T-"Lord, thank you for making me "beauty from ashes." My soul rejoices in Your love for me! Thank you for living in me and making me able to be a friend to others in your love."

S-" Lord, I desire that the world would see how I love others and see You in me. Lord, help me speak with grace, and love others purely with a heart like yours when offenses occur."

"If you want to understand the Bible, get on your knees... You will learn more in one hour of prayerful communion with the Spirit than in a thousand years in all the schools of human culture."
~A. T. Pierson~

DIGGING DEEPER

A bit more about Timothy...

What does Paul call himself and Timothy in Philippians 1:1?

_____

What is the definition of that kind of person?

_____

How does Paul describe Timothy in 1 Timothy 1:18?

_____

What had Timothy experienced, according to Hebrews 13:23?

_____

What more do you learn about Timothy in Philippians 2:12-23? _____

_____

_____

_____

DAY FOUR

ON MY KNEES:

As you settle in to spend some time with the Lord in His Word, begin with prayer. Sometimes we tend to rush through our time in prayer in an effort to get to our favorite part of the study or to "just get it done and check-marked off our list". Resist hurrying through your study and consider that the Lord is delighted to spend this time with you.

Pray. "O Lord, my Lord, how great is Your name in all the earth. How amazing, how wonderful that You care so deeply about me that You would send Your son to die for me, even when I was still in sin! I want to know You and love You more!"

Write. Today, write the simple, straight-forward commands of 1 Corinthians 16:13-14. Think on these words and prayerfully commit them to action through the power of God that is within you!_____

_____

_____

_____

Read. Before you begin to investigate 2 Timothy further, begin first by reading all four chapters. Continuing to do this may sound unnecessarily repetitive, but it will help you build a foundation for all that you will learn in the following weeks.

INVESTIGATIVE STUDY
AERIAL

Apply!

A crucial part of your AERIAL VIEW observations is gaining an understanding of the historical times and context of the book you are studying. As Paul penned his letter to Timothy, Nero was reigning over Rome as an insane tyrant and increasingly persecuting Christians. Eventually, Paul, Peter and Timothy would be martyred during his rule. Indeed, Paul's encouragement to Timothy and his need for encouragement from Timothy was critical as the world around them became more violently opposed to the gospel. Many seemingly-solid believers were turning away from Jesus, ashamed of the testimony of the Lord. Today, we will turn to modern day history reviews for a look at the days and times of Paul and Timothy.

The AD 60's World Summarized:

Stretching from modern day Europe, to Africa, to the Middle East, the Roman Empire in 64 AD encompassed a majority of the civilized world; and at its core was the lively city of Rome. Much like an ancient New York City, Rome had a bustling, diverse population. Religion played a key part in Roman culture – from family shrines within homes, to extravagant temples of various gods in the city itself. Politics and government were important parts of the ancient Roman culture as well. Philosophers such as Socrates, Plato, and Aristotle influenced literature and philosophy. The class system made the daily routine for the rich quite different than the daily routine for the poor; Those who were rich had nicer houses, more extravagant modes of transportation (such as riding on elephants to dinner), and much more leisurely lives with servants present to fulfill their every desire. Those who were poor lived in much smaller, squalid houses, and labored every moment of their lives. They had no slaves to grant their wishes, and they sometimes served as slaves themselves. However, there was one large aspect of the ancient Roman culture that united both the rich and poor classes: the Circus Maximus – an arena in which man would fight against man, beast would fight against beast, man and beast would fight against each other – all to the death. This sport, while gruesome, was free to the public and heavily enjoyed by the entire Roman civilization.

Life for Christians in the ancient Roman culture was quite different from the rest of society. Obviously, the Christians' view of religion differed greatly from the polytheistic beliefs of the Roman culture. Instead of looking to the philosophers that the Romans looked to, the Christians studied the Holy Scriptures for wisdom, guidance, and the answers to life's questions. Life was different for the Christians in regard to the Circus Maximus as well. Christians were not spectators of the activity, rather, they were viewed as the entertainment.

The grotesque persecution of the Christians began to greatly escalate in 64 AD. While Stephen, the first martyr, was stoned to death in 35 AD, it was in 64 AD that the Christians were blamed by Nero for the Great Fire of Rome, resulting in widespread hate and persecution from the government and the citizens. Under Nero's rule, Christians were crucified, mauled to death by wild animals, and set on fire to serve as evening lights in Nero's gardens. While there is speculation on how many Christians were killed as a result of Roman persecution, it has been estimated that 100,000 Christians were martyred for their faith in Jesus Christ between the first and third centuries. Christian icons such as the apostles Peter and Paul died as a result of persecution during this time.

How do you think that these times would affect the spread of the gospel?

_____

How were Christians suffering?

_____

Why do you think Christians would consider giving up their faith?

_____

Paul's "World" Summarized:

Paul tells us in 2 Timothy 2:9 that he was in prison as a criminal. History tells us that he wrote his letter between AD 64-67. Learn more about the Roman prisons of this time from the paragraph below.

Modern day prisons tend to serve more as rehabilitation centers, rather than places of cruel and unusual punishment. Time for work, recreation and education are involved in the daily schedule of most inmates; and special programs have been specifically designed for self betterment in the prison system. Modern day prisons, however, are not quite accurate depictions of prisons in ancient Rome. The Mamertine Prison, where the apostle Paul penned his second letter to Timothy, was quite the dungeon.

Previous to its use as a prison, the Mamertine was thought to be used as a cistern. The circular bottom room, known as the "tullianum" served as the dark, damp, holding room for prisoners. The upper room, known as the "carcer" provided the only access to the lower room: a hole in the floor through which the prisoners were lowered. Regardless of the weather outside, the lower dungeon was never dry, and it was certainly never warm.

Besides the physical trials experienced while being held in the Mamertine Prison, many prisoners faced sociological trials as well. During the Apostle Paul's first imprisonment in Rome, he was held under house arrest; an honorable sentence which was reserved for high status prisoners, or those convicted of non-serious crimes. The Mamertine Prison, however, was specially reserved for significant state prisoners accused of serious crimes. Prisoners who were held in the Mamertine would be the equivalent of a modern day prisoner convicted of committing treason against the United States. Association with a Mamertine prisoner was not desired.

Why do you think all of Paul's companions would have deserted him?

_____

How do you think Paul's circumstances could have discouraged him?

_____

After having read 2 Timothy four times, how do you think Paul handled his circumstances?

_____

_____

Understanding the lay of the land:

Look over the map of Paul and Timothy's day. Take a moment to fill in where Paul and Timothy were located as well as the other locations Paul mentions in 2 Timothy.

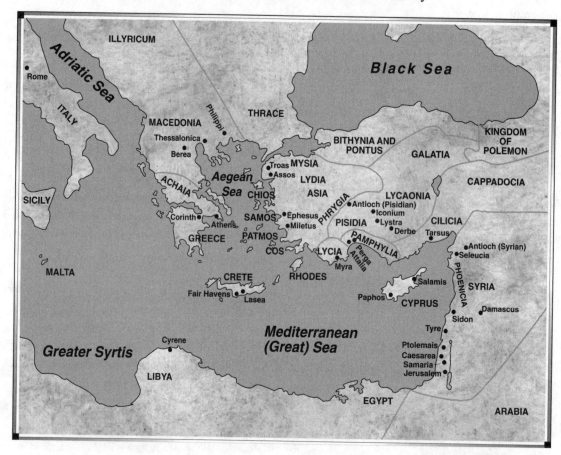

There not easy times for Paul and Timothy as followers of Jesus Christ. Not only were the ruling world leaders persecuting them, there was trouble growing within the churches they started and led. The faithful (or not so faithful) were fleeing for the hills in fear and disobedience.

Paul sat alone, imprisoned in Rome and awaiting his certain death. Surprisingly, a confident and bold charge resounds from the depths of a Roman prison to Timothy and to us. With further study, the Lord's message will become clearer through studying this tender, fatherly-toned letter of encouragement and exhortation. Soon Timothy would be among the next generation of leaders. He needed encouragement and strong direction. We do too, don't we?

So, my fellow believer, continue to carry on deeper into this book as we have only just begun to see what the Lord has in store for us in our study. There is so much packed into these short four chapters of 2 Timothy! Hopefully, your excitement about what you are learning is rising!

APPLY!

Did you hear a sense of urgency in Paul's letter? Maybe you heard discouragement or encouragement. Look for the verse(s) that invokes what you felt was one of the overriding moods of the letter; write the reference and emotion here:

_____

Think for a moment about what you wrote. Is there a Scripture that comes to mind that addresses this emotion? Use your Bible concordance to find a verse that would be helpful if you were experiencing such a feeling. Write the passage reference here:

_____

Do you know someone who is experiencing this? Grab a card or a high tech communication tool and send off a note of sharing the passage you found with the person that God brings to mind.

A . C . T . S .   P R A Y E R   T I M E

As Paul shares with us in 2 Timothy, we are going to struggle and suffer for the gospel. There will be times of discouragement and fear, especially if we focus on our own strength and forget that we have access to the ultimate strength…our God! Open your Bible to Joshua 1:8-9. Read the passage and then close your time in prayer.

A "Lord, You are omnipresent and ever-caring. I praise You because You deeply care about me as Your child."

C "Lord, I confess that I become anxious and react timidly at times. Forgive me for not resting in Your strength and depending on my own."

T "Thank you Lord, I am grateful for Your continued protection and presence in my life as I grow in my salvation. I am blessed by Your promises to make my way prosperous and successful."

S "Lord, help me to not only be strong and courageous, but faithful in meditating on Your Word so that I can be careful to do what You have instructed me to do. I know that this is only possible in Your strength. Amen."

"A well-worn Bible is a sign of a well-fed soul, and a Bible that's falling apart usually belongs to someone whose life isn't!"
~Anonymous~

DAY FIVE

ON MY KNEES:

Welcome to the conclusion of Week 1 of your Sword Study and thus, the end of our AERIAL VIEW of 2 Timothy. You have done well! The Lord promises great things to those who hunger after His Word. Let's pray.

Pray. "Father, I want to be still. As I finish this week, there have been times when I have grown weary. I want my mind and heart to be quieted so that I might come to You ready and willing. Open my ears to Your message for me today. In God's mighty name I pray, amen."

Write. On the lines below, write Romans 1:16-17. _____
_____
_____

Read. Start your INVESTIGATIVE STUDY time by reading, once again, the entire letter of 2 Timothy. Try standing up while you read, to help you stay focused on God's words.

INVESTIGATIVE STUDY
AERIAL

We are about to wrap up our investigation from a big-picture level, but before we drop down to a more detailed look at 2 Timothy, let's summarize your findings thus far. Do this by temporarily titling each of the chapters and choosing what you would consider the key verse in each of them. There are no wrong answers here. Your personal titles for the chapters will help you remember what you have learned and initially observed. Fill in the blanks below.

Apply!

Chapter 1 – Title _____

Chapter 1 – Key Verse (write it out!) _____
_____

Chapter 1 – Summary Paragraph (no more than 2-3 sentences) _____
_____
_____

Chapter 2 – Title _____

Chapter 2 – Key Verse (write it out!) _____
_____

Chapter 2 – Summary Paragraph (no more than 2-3 sentences) _____
_____
_____

Chapter 3 – Title _____

Chapter 3 – Key Verse (write it out!) _____
_____

Chapter 3 – Summary Paragraph (no more than 2-3 sentences) _____
_____
_____

Chapter 4 – Title _____

Chapter 4 – Key Verse (write it out!) _____
_____

Chapter 4 – Summary Paragraph (no more than 2-3 sentences) _____
_____
_____

APPLY!

Look back one page and read Romans 1:16-17 that you wrote earlier today. Is there anyone that comes to mind that you know has faithfully stood firm and unashamed of the gospel? Take a moment today to send that person a note of encouragement. Tell him or her how you have been encouraged by his or her faith. Think of those that are in your life and those you see from afar. The frontline soldiers need letters from the family of Christ!

Keep this person or people in your prayers as they could be undergoing suffering in the name of Christ.

A.C.T.S. PRAYER TIME

Open your Bible to Psalm 24:8 and use it as a starting point for your closing prayer time with the Lord. *Adore* Him as the Creator, who has dominion over all things. *Confess* that there are times in which you act as though you are the one in control. *Thank* Him that you know Him personally. *Ask* Him to show His might and strength in your life.

A -"God of all the earth and everything that is in it, may Your name be lifted on high by all who know You."

C –"Forgive me Father that I do not continually give you the praise and glory that You deserve as the King of Glory."

T –"I am so very grateful that You accept me as I am, wrap Your arms around me and show Your lovingkindness to me over and over throughout each day."

S –"Lord of hosts, King of glory and God of my salvation, go before me in all that this day will bring and show Yourself to me in what I see, hear and do. Remind me of our time together today. In Your great and powerful name I pray. Amen."

*"If I were the devil, one of my first aims would be to
stop folk from digging into the Bible."*
~J.I. Packer~

DIGGING DEEPER

On the first day of our study, we learned quite a bit about Paul as the author of 2 Timothy. In Philippians 3:4-8, Paul gives us a list of all that his peers might have counted towards his greatness according to the world's standards. In verses 7 and 8, Paul gives his summation of what was important. These verses are a call to us today to count knowing our Lord and Savior, Jesus Christ, as our highest possession. Commit these verses to memory!

UNASHAMED: RICHARD WURMBRAND

I don't look like much, I know. My pages are faded, my binding torn. Some people wouldn't recognize me as God's Word. But my hard-earned rips and wrinkles all came from years of adventures with my owner, Richard Wurmbrand.

You might say I have a Romanian accent. A friend gave me to Richard soon after he and his wife Sabina, both Jewish Romanians, received Christ in 1938. That's how our story began.

When Richard and Sabina chose to follow their Messiah, they did so in a big way. Soon, Richard became an ordained minister. As he and his wife took the gospel to their fellow Jews, my pages grew worn with near-constant use.

Soon, the tramping of feet and the shouts of angry soldiers filled the air. The Germans had occupied Romania. To avoid prison, many Jews went into hiding, but not Richard and Sabina.

I went along as Richard, unashamed of the gospel, preached in crowded bomb shelters. I waited inside his shirt as he rescued Jewish children. More than once, I found myself thrown to the ground as officers arrested and beat him. But somehow, Richard always managed to rescue me. And somehow, God took care of him, too.

Danger Ahead

1945 brought Communism and the Russian invasion of Richard's beloved homeland. As life became more dangerous, he spent more time in my pages. During one key meeting, he stood alone against hundreds of leaders to give a bold challenge to Communism. My words—God's words—gave him the strength he needed.

Soon, Richard and Sabina set about winning the Russians to

Christ. He and his church tossed hundreds of others like me into the open windows of trains filled with Russian soldiers. People say that between 1945 and 1947, he distributed one million Bibles to Russian troops and smuggled other copies into Russia himself.

Many of the Russians kept these holy books, and many received the Savior. But on February 29, 1948, it happened: the secret police arrested Richard Wurmbrand. My once-gilt-edged pages trembled, but he stood bold and strong.

At police headquarters, officers locked us in a solitary cell. Richard describes the horrors like this:

A number of us decided to pay the price for the privilege of preaching, so we accepted their terms. It was a deal: we preached and they beat us. We were happy preaching; they were happy beating us—so everyone was happy.—Tortured for Christ

Once again, he was unashamed of the gospel. Although Sabina was arrested while he was in prison, she was released several years before her husband. For a time, the Wurmbrand's nine-year-old son, Mihai, was alone and homeless. But God hadn't forsaken them—and they knew it.

Upon Sabina's release, officials told her Richard had died in prison. But he and I were still there, bringing light to the darkness. For more than eight years, Richard and I remained in prison. He endured starvation, illness, beatings, and other unspeakable tortures.

As his body grew weaker, his faith grew stronger. By the time he was released and told never to preach again, he was a mighty warrior. His trials left him faith-full and fear-less, ready to change the world.

From Trials to Triumph

Richard was also ready to ignore the warnings and work with the underground church once more. In 1959, a coworker betrayed him and he again went to prison. My pages were falling out, but I was glad to bring him comfort when the officers shoved him into the cell. For the next five years, the two of us remained in that dreary place.

Once again, Richard's trials only made him stronger. When he tasted freedom again in 1964, he would not look back.

At first, Richard didn't want to leave Romania and the still-suffering believers. But his friends convinced him he could become a voice for the underground church. He moved his family to the United States, where they saw God do great things.

In America, I sat in a place of honor on his bedside table. But he still picked me up to read favorite passages. I listened as he testified before Congress, stripping off his shirt to reveal a back covered with the scars of many wounds. I watched as he began a ministry, The Voice of the Martyrs, which highlights the cause of the persecuted church.

I knew the Father was smiling at the ways His Word was working out in the life of Richard Wurmbrand, unashamed of the gospel. And in my own way, I was smiling, too.

D A Y   O N E

ON MY KNEES:

Welcome to a fresh, new week as we head toward a deeper level of discovery in 2 Timothy! You spent last week surveying the whole book through an aerial view in order to gain a big picture of Paul's letter to Timothy. This week and next, we will focus on taking a closer look at the first chapter. Settle into the place that you set aside to sit at the Lord's feet and let's begin with prayer.

Pray. "In You, oh Lord, I take refuge. As I begin today, I want to behold Your face within Your Word. Impress Your words on my heart that I might live righteously for Your sake. Amen."

Write. Today, you will begin your own copy of the book of 2 Timothy. Begin by prayerfully writing verses 1 and 2 in the *"Write!"* section of your Sword Study.

Read. Meditate on each word of Chapter 1 as you thoughtfully read the passage before beginning your INVESTIGATIVE STUDY portion of your Sword Study.

INVESTIGATIVE STUDY
STREETVIEW

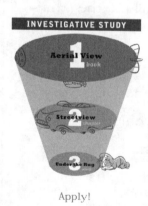

Apply!

We are going to explore 2 Timothy from a STREETVIEW perspective this week. The STREETVIEW focuses on one chapter at a time and can involve one or more exercises. First, we will interview the chapter by asking "who, what, when, where, why, and how" questions. Then, we will make general observations of the chapter by looking for exhortations, commands, topics, or lists. Finally, we will search the chapter for any key words. Key words are words that are repeated or appear to be the focus of several verses within the chapter.

During the "interview" process, our goal is to gain deeper understanding of the text in smaller sections. We will accomplish this by asking short, simple questions of the text.

Verses 1 to 5, "The Greeting"

What two positions does Paul claim to hold (one in the church and one over Timothy)?

_____

In Whom is the promise of life found?_____

How does Paul view Timothy? _____

For what does Paul thank God in verse 3? _____

How is Paul serving? _____

What does Paul do day and night? _____

What was the cause of Timothy's tears? (see Acts 20:37-38) _____

_____

Why does Paul want to see Timothy? _____

What attribute does Paul recall in Timothy? _____

Verses 6 to 12, "Don't Be Ashamed, I'm Not!"

What word implies that Timothy might need encouragement to get back to using his gift?

_____

What is the opposite of a spirit of fear/timidity? _____

What two things does Paul say should not bring shame to Timothy? _____

_____

What is the testimony of the Lord? _____

What does God's power enable us to do for the sake of the gospel? _____

Why isn't Paul ashamed of the gospel, according to verse 12? _____

Verses 13-14, "So do this:"

What two exhortations/commands does Paul give Timothy in these verses?

_____

_____

What has been committed/entrusted to us as believers in Christ? _____

Verses 15-18, "Be Aware – Be Warned"

How many believers from Asia had left Paul? _____

Why did Paul ask that mercy be given to Onesiphorus' household? _____

APPLY!

Have you ever been ashamed of the gospel? Think back on the situation. Is there anything someone could have said to you to encourage you to be unashamed? Write yourself a note of encouragement using a passage from 2 Timothy (or elsewhere) to help train your mind to dwell on God's Word and stand unabashedly for the gospel.

A.C.T.S. PRAYER TIME

Jesus has done so much for us! In your time of *Adoration*, focus on one aspect of God's character that He has shown to all Christians. Did the Holy Spirit convict you by any of Paul's words to Timothy? If so, *Confess* it! Paul was thankful for many believers. Think of those in your life that encourage you in your faith and *Thank* God for them today. In your time of *Supplication*, ask God to create within you a sincere faith…start by asking Him to show you what it means to have a "sincere faith."

A – 'Lord, I praise You for Your mercy and how You saved me!"

C – "Forgive me Lord for those times when I was ashamed of being bold about the gospel with my friends that do not know You."

T – "Thank you for parents who encourage me to study Your Word and have shared their faith in You with me."

S – "Lord, I long to be an encouragement to my friends when they are going through hard times. I want to have a sincere faith like Timothy."

"Never let good books take the place of the Bible.
Drink from the Well, not from the streams that flow from the Well."
~ Amy Carmichael~

DAY TWO

ON MY KNEES:

Welcome back, fellow student of the Word! Are you ready for a time of revelation and encouragement in your daily walk? We do not have to wander aimlessly or fritter our time away as followers of Christ. We are charged with an eternal purpose of glorifying God in all we say and do. The Bible is His textbook and the Spirit is our guide. Come before Him in prayer.

Pray. "God, You are my strength and a Strong Tower in times of trouble. I don't want to decipher Your Word in my own strength and knowledge. Humbly, I come, on my knees before Your throne, desiring and requesting through the Holy Spirit's help to hear you speak through Your inspired, inerrant Word. Disciple me, Lord. In Jesus' powerful name, I ask. "

Write. Turn to your *"Write!"* tab in the back of your Sword Study pages. Carefully write 2 Timothy 1:3-4, concentrating on each word, recognizing that you are copying God's words to you.

Read. After you read 2 Timothy, Chapter 1, we will move to the next stage of investigation in our STREETVIEW.

INVESTIGATIVE STUDY
STREETVIEW

Apply!

Now we are ready to look for lists, exhortations or commands, and key words in Chapter 1. Looking at these will help us understand the main points that Paul is trying to drill into our hearts and minds as his readers. We will begin with the lists.

Lists of 2 Timothy 1

In 2 Timothy 1:7, Paul gives us a list describing the type of spirit that God gives us. List the three attributes here:

_____

_____

_____

What does it sound like Timothy may have been struggling with, that did not come from God?

_____

Paul uses the word and synonyms of the word "remember" four times in the first chapter. List what Paul tells Timothy he has either remembered or wants Timothy to remember in the following verses:

2 Timothy 1:3 _____

2 Timothy 1:4 _____

2 Timothy 1:5 _____

2 Timothy 1:6 _____

According to verses 8 through 10, Paul calls us to join him in his suffering for the gospel. We are to do this by the power of God. Paul then lists all that the power of God has accomplished on our behalf. List the five verbs that describe what God has done.(Hint: verses 9a and 10b)

_____   _____   _____   _____   _____

Our final list is a sub-list of the above, and is found in verse 10b. What three things were done through Jesus Christ as our Savior? Take the extra time and effort to write out full sentences in your answers. How good to be reminded of His great work on our behalf!

God's power through Jesus _____

God's power through Jesus _____

God's power through Jesus _____

Exhortations of 2 Timothy 1
Look up the following verses in 2 Timothy Chapter 1 and summarize Paul's exhortations.
Verse 6 _____

Verse 8 _____
_____
_____

Verse 13 _____

Verse 14 _____

The People of Chapter 1
Ordinarily, we would note the people of a particular book when we are at the overview level of our study, but Paul mentions so many people that we are going to take a moment during each chapter's review to take note of them.

On the lines below, write down the names or references to people that Paul mentions in Chapter 1. Next to their name or description include a short observation concerning them. (Do not include any observations about the Trinity at this time.) We have done the first one for you!

Person(s)	Observation
Timothy	Main recipient, spiritual son of Paul

APPLY!

What is your favorite type of worship music? Can you think of a song that encourages you to stand boldly? Take time to write out the lyrics and send them to a friend or, if you are able, send a link to the song on YouTube.

A.C.T.S. PRAYER TIME

A – "Praise You, Lord, that You are an all-powerful God. It was Your power that saved me and that gives me the ability to live for You."

C- "I confess that there are times I do things in my own strength and take control of my life. Forgive me for not trusting You to work through me."

T – "Thank You for giving me the power to do the right thing when others wanted me to go along with the crowd."

S – "Lord, I want to have Your power working in and through me every day so that You will be glorified."

"Without the present illumination of the Holy Spirit, the Word of God
must remain a dead letter to every man, no matter how intelligent or well-educated he may be...
It is just as essential for the Holy Spirit to reveal the truth of Scripture
to the reader today as it was necessary for him to inspire the writers in their day."
~William Law~

DAY THREE

ON MY KNEES:

Friend in Christ, be mindful that you are showing your faith even as you come to do your study today. Keep coming! The Lord will meet you and empower your days. Ask Him for insight; surely He will answer your request because You are asking in accordance with His will.

Pray. "Lord, You are the King of kings forever and ever. Help me to see Your power and might clearly in my study of Your precepts today. Settle my thoughts so that I might focus on my time with You. I want to pay attention to You as a good student so that I might apply what I learn to how I live. "

Write. Please write 2 Timothy 1:5.

Read. Once again, before our INVESTIGATIVE STUDY portion, begin by reading 2 Timothy, Chapter 1.

Apply!

INVESTIGATIVE STUDY
UNDER THE RUG: KEY WORDS AND WORD STUDIES

Today, you are going to look for key words. A key word is a word that is repeated or contributes to the central meaning of the text. Carefully re-read Chapter 1 and mark the key words with your own symbols as you read. After you mark all of your key words, list them here with your symbol and a definition from a Bible dictionary or an online resource:

Symbol	Key word	Definition
_____	_____	_____
_____	_____	_____
_____	_____	_____
_____	_____	_____
_____	_____	_____
_____	_____	_____

Word Study:

Below you will find an abbreviated overview of the three-part Word Study process; Word Studies will be a part of each chapter study. In preparation for tomorrow, briefly review the Word Study process so you will be able to put it into practice as you go UNDER THE RUG tomorrow.

In PART A: We will look up the Greek word in the Strong's Concordance and discover the Strong's number for the key word by looking for it in the verse in which it appears.

In PART B: We will look up the number in a Greek lexicon or dictionary to discover further explanations of the word's meaning in Greek.

In PART C: We will choose the correct meaning for the use of the word in 2 Timothy.

APPLY!

It's all Greek to me! Take a few minutes and create your own alphabet and then send a short coded message to someone that considers you their Paul. A special note from an admired mentor brightens a younger one's day!

For example, your "a" could be a ☺. If you are running low on time, just write the note using a word processing program and then select the font style of wingdings or webdings! Make sure to send the key to your alphabet along with the message, so that the recipient can receive your encouraging note.

A . C . T . S .   P R A Y E R   T I M E

Close your time in prayer…

A –"The Lord is my light and salvation, whom shall I fear?" "Lord, I praise You as the God of hope who abolishes death and provides eternal life through Your Son."

C –" Forgive me for not living boldly for You, but instead find myself being timid when it comes to sharing the gospel or living for myself."

T –"Lord, thank you for giving me the privilege and Your power to share the Good News that Christ died so that we could be forgiven of all of our sins, past, present and future!

S- "Lord, give me opportunities this week to share the gospel with someone in my family that does not know Christ as Savior. Prepare the way by assuring them of my love and concern for them.

"I may no longer depend on pleasant impulses to bring me before the Lord.
I must rather respond to principles I know to be right, whether
I feel them to be enjoyable or not."
~Jim Elliot~

D I G G I N G   D E E P E R

A great way to dig deeper is to use an additional resource such as Logos Bible Software or Bible-gateway.com to do a Keyword search. Simply spend time reading the search results to gain an even better understanding of the key words from 2 Timothy.

DAY FOUR

ON MY KNEES:

Good morning…afternoon…or night! Regardless of the day or time, you have diligently arrived for a time with the Lord. Enjoy this respite. Be blessed. Start with prayer.

Pray. "Lord, give my heart sensitivity, my mind comprehension, and my spirit wisdom. Help me listen and act on what I hear in Your Word with a humble, willing heart. In Christ's name, Amen."

Write. 2 Timothy 1:6-7 is your writing task for today. As you write the words out, prayerfully ask for the characteristics of God's spirit to be displayed in your life.

Read. Before we begin a new level of study, Read through the first chapter of 2 Timothy.

INVESTIGATIVE STUDY

Apply!

INVESTIGATIVE STUDY
UNDER THE RUG:
KEY WORDS AND WORD STUDIES

The UNDER THE RUG portion of the INVESTIGATIVE STUDY is one of the most exciting parts of your Sword Study. You will dig deep beneath the surface and see things that are not evident at a cursory glance. You will gain great understanding of God and His heart as you investigate the Word in this way. UNDER THE RUG has two parts: Word Studies and Cross-references. There are many jewels hidden in God's Word! Many of them lie just beyond what the naked eye can see. We will find them by looking at the original Greek words and their meanings.

What is the Strong's Concordance?

The Strong's Concordance is a very useful tool for studying God's Word. It lists every word used in the King James Version Bible. You can look up a Bible passage, choose a key word and then look it up in the Strong's Concordance to see all the other verses that also include the same word.

Strong's is also helpful for locating Scripture verses which you remember partially but can't recall their book, chapter and/or verse. For example, you know there is a verse that says our hairs are numbered, but you aren't sure where it is in the Bible. You could look up the word "numbered" in a Strong's Concordance and it would give you a listing of all the verses that contain the word "numbered". You would then find Matthew 10:30 where God said that "the very hairs of your head are all numbered."

Each word also has a number next to it in the Strong's Concordance. The number represents a Hebrew or Greek word. In the back of the concordance Hebrew and Greek words are listed by number and explained by a short English definition. Strong's is useful even if you normally use other Bible versions, though you may need to use Bible Gateway or a KJV Bible to find the exact wording of the passage you are studying.

Word Study:

For your Word Studies, we will walk step-by-step through the process that was introduced yesterday. Choosing key words can be somewhat subjective, so you may have chosen different words than what we have chosen. After you learn the process, use the steps here to do additional study on the words that we didn't include to deepen your knowledge of God's Word.

In the first chapter of 2 Timothy, some of the words we considered were *grace, suffer/endure* and *mercy*, but the words; *gospel, faith,* and *ashamed* stood out among the others, so we will focus on these over the next several days.

PART A: As we look up the word *gospel* in the Strong's Concordance, we find that the Strong's number assigned to it in 2 Timothy 1:8, 1:10, and 2:8 is 2098. Note this because it will be used to look up a detailed explanation of the Greek word in Part B. Below is the transliteration (which is how we write the word in the English language), the pronunciation, and then the basic definition from the Strong's lexicon.

> **2098. euaggelion,** *yoo-ang-ghel'-ee-on*; from the same as *2097*; a *good message*, i.e. the *gospel:*- -gospel.

PART B: We will now look up the number 2098 in another Greek lexicon to discover a more detailed explanation of the word *gospel* in Greek:

    (II) In the writings of Paul, the gospel, that is:

        (A) Generally the gospel plan of salvation, its doctrines, declarations, precepts, promises.

        (B) By the gospel work, i.e., the preaching of the gospel, labor in the gospel.

PART A: In order to better understand the use of *gospel* in these 2 Timothy verses, we are going to look at the root word, 2097.

    2097. *gospel/preached. euaggelizo* (yoo-ang-ghel-id'-zo); from 2095 and 32; to announce good news ("evangelize") especially the gospel; declare, bring or show glad tidings, preach (the gospel).(2)

PART B: We will now look up the number 2097 in another Greek lexicon to discover a more detailed explanation of the word *gospel/preached* in Greek:

1) to bring good news, to announce glad tidings

    a) used in the OT of any kind of good news
        i) of the joyful tidings of God's kindness, in particular, of the Messianic blessings

    b) in the NT used especially of the glad tidings of the coming kingdom of God, and of the salvation to be obtained in it through Christ, and of what relates to this salvation

    c) glad tidings are brought to one, one has glad tidings proclaimed to him

    d) to proclaim glad tidings
        i) instruct men concerning the things that pertain to Christian salvation [1]

Both 2 Timothy 1:8 and 1:10 refer to "the gospel plan of salvation", while 2 Timothy 2:8 refers to "the preaching of the *gospel*", which is a different form of *gospel*. This word wraps the ideas of preaching and good news into one verb. Let's take a closer look at these verses to see how the definitions help us better understand how Paul used the word *gospel*.

Gospel in 2 Timothy

Read 2 Timothy 1:8.
What phrase does Paul use as a synonym to the word *gospel* in this verse?

_____

Read 2 Timothy 1:10.
What two things were brought to light through the *gospel*?

_____

Read 2 Timothy 2:8.
Here we see that Paul was indeed preaching the *gospel*. What two points did he highlight in this passage? _____

Tomorrow, we will look at the word *euaggelion* throughout the Scriptures so that we might gain a better understanding as we see it used. We will see how God has reached out to man in a variety of ways through His inspired writers and bearers of the Good News. For indeed, "The Lord is not slow to fulfill his promise as some count slowness, but is patient toward you, not wishing that any should perish, but that all should reach repentance." 2 Peter 3:9 ESV

APPLY!

Take a moment to write out the gospel in your own words, just as though you were sharing the Good News with someone who asked you about the hope you "seem to have".

The gospel in _____ words:

_____

_____

_____

_____

A.C.T.S. PRAYER TIME

What a privilege it is to know that God is one who gives over and over to those who are His! "For God so loved the world He gave His only begotten Son…" This week we looked at the meaning of the Greek word for "*gospel*". Adore God as the giver of eternal life. Confess those times when sharing the gospel with certain friends seems impossible. Thank Jesus for giving His life for you and the person who shared the Good News with you. When you come to the time of Supplication, ask Him to remind you of His promise to give you the power to share the gospel when you have an opportunity to share your faith.

A - "Lord, I praise You for being the One who always gives of Yourself even to the point of sending Your Son to die for me."

C - "This week it became so apparent that I need to remember that you have given me the POWER! I confess it never even occurred to me to trust in your power to give the gospel until I saw this truth in 2 Timothy 1:7."

T - "Thank You, Lord for the gift of righteousness in Christ without which I could not stand before You cleansed of all my sins.

S - "Lord, I really want to be available to You, when I am with my friends, to take every situation as an opportunity to give testimony about You trusting in Your power."

"Thank You, Lord for the gift of righteousness in Christ without which I could not stand before You cleansed of all my sins."

"Is prayer your steering wheel or your spare tire?"
~Corrie Ten Boom ~

DIGGING DEEPER

When you began your study today, you wrote out verse 7 of 2 Timothy. Do you know what the word "discipline" means in this context? Go on a short rabbit trail and find out! The gospel is clearly worth being in prison according to Paul. Turn to Luke 9:18-26. Jesus tells us in this passage what He desires from us as we consider the gospel. Why not memorize Luke 9:23-26 as a way to remember what our Savior asks of us.

DAY FIVE

ON MY KNEES:

How are you doing today? Has this been a good week? Has it been long, short, tiring or relaxing? Sometimes it feels so good to arrive at a weekend. We look forward to the change of pace, special plans or even just resting after a busy week. Let's get comfortable and be strengthened through the study of God's Word. Pray first, though.

Pray. "Father, You are the God who never grows weary. You do not need to rest, yet You call us to rest in You and cast all of our cares into Your fathomless arms. Help me to live my life without anxiousness and a sincere faith as though I believe these truths. I want to fight a good fight by Your might! In Your everlasting, powerful name I pray."

Write. Today, write 2 Timothy 1:8-9 in the *"Write!"* section of your notebook. Ask the Holy Spirit to begin speaking to your heart of ways that you can rejoice in your calling

Read. Before we begin to travel around the Scriptures to learn of the various uses of the word *gospel*, read 2 Timothy, Chapter 1. Today, maybe you can gather a younger sibling or call a grandparent to read back and forth through the verses. Perhaps, you might even just read the whole book as you wrap up this week? Onward!

INVESTIGATIVE STUDY
UNDER THE RUG: CROSS REFERENCES

Apply!

In yesterday's study of the *gospel*, we learned the Biblical definition. Today, we will see the word in use around the Scriptures to gain a better understanding of all that it means. Prepare for "sword drills", boot up your laptop or prepare your handheld, as we will be visiting several Scriptures on our journey. Let's begin.

Read Matthew 4:23-25* and answer the following questions:

Who was proclaiming the *gospel* in these verses?

_____

With whom did He share the *gospel*?

_____

Where did He share the *gospel*?

_____

What was the result of His boldness?

According to Mark 8:35, what will happen if you give your life for the *gospel*?

What happens to those who do not obey the *gospel* of Jesus, according to 2 Thessalonians 1:7-9?

Turn to 1 Corinthians 15:1-4 and answer the following questions:

What three things were done according to verse 1?

What does verse 2 say about being saved?

Why did Jesus die, according to verse 3?

What was delivered as first importance, *gospel*, according to verses 3 and 4?

Read Romans 10:8-15 and answer the following questions:

In verse 8, what is to be preached?

How is a person saved, according to verse 9?

How does verse 15 summarize what the preachers bring?

What two things are to be done with the *gospel*, according to Mark 1:15?

_____   _____

Who is the *gospel* for, according to Luke 2:10? _____

Does the *gospel* need to be presented in cleverness, according to 1 Corinthians 1:17?

Has someone shared the "Good News" with you? Have you shared the "Good News" of the *gospel* with someone? Pause for a moment in prayer. "Lord, soften my heart right now for what You want me to hear as I conclude my study in Your Word today."

APPLY!

According to Romans 10:9-10, those who have "confessed with their mouths that Jesus is Lord" and "believed in their hearts that God raised Jesus from the dead" will be saved. "For with the heart man believes, resulting in righteousness, and with the mouth he confesses, resulting in salvation."

Is this true of you? If not, what is stopping you from doing that right now? Consider this day whom you will serve.

If this is true of you, then you are commanded to tell others about the "Good News"!

When an opportunity opens up, it may feel somewhat scary, but be faithful and share Christ's love and truth with your friend. The more your life reflects Christ's character and love, the more your words will ring true; you can always describe the grace that you have been given, so don't pass up the chance! Pray about this now, that you will have the courage to share the gospel in every opportunity and situation that God puts in your life.

There are many different tools to help you learn to share the gospel with others. Take a few minutes to create your own tract using 1 Corinthians 15:1-4.

A.C.T.S. PRAYER TIME

Fill-in your A.C.T.S. Prayer Time lines based on what you learned about the gospel and your "Apply!" section.

A - *Adoration* _____

C - *Confession* _____

T - *Thanksgiving* _____

S - *Supplication* _____

"We used every modern means to reach the ear of the unconverted ... and then punched them straight between the eyes with the Gospel."
~Billy Graham~

DIGGING DEEPER:

There are literally hundreds of passages throughout the Bible with the word(s) for *gospel*. Spend some time looking up some of these additional verses. Take out a separate piece of paper and write the reference and a short summary of what you learn about the *gospel* in them.

Mark 16:15, Acts 14:15, Romans 1:9, Romans 2:16, 1 Corinthians 9:12, Galatians 1:10-12, Galatians 3:8, Ephesians 1:13, Philippians 1:16, Philippians 1:27, Colossians 1:4-6, 1 Thessalonians 1:5, Revelations 14:6.

HE IS ABLE: PERPETUA'S DIARY

How does it feel to be condemned to die?

History holds an amazing record of this exact experience. The diary of Perpetua, a young North African believer, tells the story of the days between her imprisonment and death as a martyr in 202 AD.

The problem: Second-century language doesn't communicate well to modern ears. Please enjoy this present-day adaptation in which Perpetua's diary becomes a series of blog posts.

DAY 1: NO OTHER NAME

Arrested. I never thought it would happen, but it did. When Daddy, who doesn't believe, realized what was happening, he tried to shake my determination to stand up under such pressure.

"Dad," I said, "See this vase?"

"Sure."

"Could we call it a broom, a truck, or anything else?"

"No way. It is what it is."

"And so am I. No other name besides 'Christian' fits."

Fire blazed in his eyes as he made a quick, angry motion—then stopped. In another moment, he left. He and his arguments disappeared.

I don't know what the future holds, but I know the One I trust.

....

DAY 6: REST

Long days. Desperate times. But today, two kind, believing friends bribed the soldiers to move my friends and me into a better part of the prison for a few hours. The quieter, cleaner atmosphere brought us rest and peace.

Soon afterward, my family brought my son so I could nurse him. My mother and brother seem so torn up. Watching them hurt is worse than my own pain.

But guess what God did? He made a way for me to keep my baby with me! This precious gift of time took away my worry and turned my prison into a palace. Suddenly, I'd choose to stay here rather than anywhere else.

Thanks for that gift, Father. And thanks for your faithfulness. Always.

....

DAY 17: VISION

God speaks through dreams and visions. I accept that as truth. But what if the vision reveals something you'd rather not see?

Not long ago, I asked God to use a vision to show me the future. So why was I surprised when He did?

I saw a narrow ladder that reached up to the heavens. Its sides carried sharp, spiked metal weapons, designed to keep people away.

I almost stayed away myself. A gruesome dragon lay at the ladder's base, but I followed my friend upward with only a small hesitation. At the top, we found a beautiful garden, thousands of people in white, and a white-robed shepherd. The cool sweetness of the sheep's milk he gave us woke me up to share my dream with my brother.

We agree on its meaning: Our hope lies not in this world. Suffering will come before heaven's sweetness. And we are not ashamed. We know whom we have believed, and He—only He—is able.

....

DAY 24: INTERRUPTION

A few days have passed. People whispered about a hearing. Soon, Daddy came again to persuade me away from my faith.

"If you won't think about yourself, think about your family," he pleaded. "Your death will destroy us all, from young to old. If you persist, none of us will ever speak freely again."

He spoke out of his deep love. How could I not feel his hurt? But as a follower of Christ, how could I follow his instructions?

"Daddy," I responded. "All will go according to the Father's will. Our fates rest in His hands—not those of man."

He left, his face stony. I wept. I had no other choice.

....

DAY 35: STEADFAST

More days have passed. Today, the guards rushed us off for our hearing.

One by one, my comrades admitted their guilt. My turn, and Daddy again appeared with my baby. "Perform the sacrifice!" he said. "Save yourself and your child!"

The governor added his voice: "Don't you care about either your father or your child? Offer the sacrifice to our rulers!"

I had no choice. "I bow to no emperor, no governor, no earthly king. I will offer no worship except to my God."

....

A short time later, Perpetua and her four comrades were killed in a brutal stadium celebration. She remained steadfast in her resolve never to worship anyone but the one true God.

Perpetua knew whom she believed—and He was able.

Adapted from "The Martyrdom of Saints Felicita and Perpetua," http://www.pbs.org/wgbh/pages/frontline/shows/religion/maps/primary/perpetua.html

DAY ONE

ON MY KNEES:

Are you blessed with many friends joining you in the study of 2 Timothy? Or is the Lord teaching you to stand strong even when there are few joining you? Our God works all things together for those who love Him. Trust Him for He is trustworthy. Let's go to Him in prayer and share what's on our hearts.

Pray. "God of all ages, You are King forever and ever. Help me to see Your power and might clearly in the study and application of Your precepts. Settle my thoughts so that I might focus during my time at the foot of Your throne."

Write. Please open up your Sword Study to the section marked *"Write!"* and write out 2 Timothy 1:10-11.

Read. Guess what? We are going to request that you read Chapter 1 of 2 Timothy again today. When campers are far from home, young missionaries move miles away from family, or soldiers are stationed across oceans, a letter from home can be their lifeline. They may be alone and discouraged, but the words of encouragement from loved ones make all the difference in the world. Just as they would read, and re-read, and re-read that letter, we want you to do the same with the Word of God. Persevere, my fellow student of the Word, persevere and read on!

INVESTIGATIVE STUDY
UNDER THE RUG: KEY WORDS AND WORD STUDIES

Faith is the second word we will study in depth. While it appears twice in the first chapter, *faith* is found in every chapter for a total of eight instances in 2 Timothy.

After we look at the word study of *faith*, we will look at the each of its uses in 2 Timothy and then read it in cross references throughout the Scriptures to gain a deeper knowledge of what Paul meant when he used the word *faith* throughout his letter.

PART A: If you were to look up the word *faith* in Strong's Concordance, you would find that the Strong's number assigned to it in 2 Timothy is 4102. We will use this number to look up the detailed explanation of the Greek word in Part B. Below are the transliteration (the way the word is written in English), the pronunciation, and the basic definition from the Strong's lexicon (dictionary).

4102. *Faith. Pistis pis'-tis*, from 3982; persuasion, i.e. credence; conviction (of religious truth, or the truthfulness of God or a religious teacher); Especially reliance upon Christ for salvation.

PART B: If you look up the number 4102 in another Greek lexicon, you can discover further explanations of the meaning of *faith* in Greek as seen here:

   1) to win over or persuade

   2) a firm and confiding belief in Jesus and His gospel (2 Timothy 1:5, 2:18)

   3) to be trusted, reliable (2 Timothy 2:13*, 22)

   4) *faith* professed (2 Timothy 4:7)

   Synonym: act of assurance, confirmation, reliance, confidence, belief firmly held, doctrine and truth

   Antonym: confusion, unbelief, ungodly, departure from the truth, blasphemy, hypocrisy, falsehood.

PART C: As you read through those explanations, open your Bible to the various passages noted in 2 Timothy that we have included within PART B.

Highlight every instance of the word *faith* in your Bible, then answer the following questions.

According to 2 Timothy 1:13, where is *faith* found?

_____

What happens to some men when they hear false teachings, as noted in 2 Timothy 2:18?

_____

In 2 Timothy 2:22:
What is a characteristic of someone who has *faith*?

_____

What are we to do regarding *faith*, according to this verse?

_____

How do we do this?

_____

Who rejected *faith* in 2 Timothy 3:8?

_____

Who followed Paul's *faith* in 2 Timothy 3:10?

_____

According to 2 Timothy 3:15, to what does *faith* in Jesus Christ lead?

_____

In 2 Timothy 4:7, what does Paul say constitutes a "good fight" or a "finished course"?

_____

Clearly, *faith* was heavy on Paul's mind as he intertwined it throughout his letter to Timothy. As we continue our study, we will refer back to this word study of *faith* often, as a reference point.

APPLY!

Do you have *faith* in Jesus?
If you do, list out what convinced you to believe in His name:

_____

_____

_____

_____

If you don't have a solid *faith* in Jesus or there are some things that are difficult for you to understand or believe, write them on the lines below:

_____

_____

_____

_____

A.C.T.S. PRAYER TIME

"A firm and confiding belief in Jesus" is what God calls us to through the pen of Paul. Close your day in prayer with your Bible open to Psalm 130. Use this short Psalm to ignite your prayer of Adoration. Next, use the Psalm to lead you as you pray through Confession, Thanksgiving, and Supplication. Do you find it difficult to have faith for a God you cannot see? If so, confess that to Him. Do you lack trust in Him with your life? Confess that too. Thank Him for the faith that He has given you and ask Him to strengthen it through the study of His word.

A - "Lord, I praise you for being attentive to my voice, for hearing my confessions and supplications, and for not only granting me forgiveness, but also abundantly blessing me with Your daily glorious presence and provisions."

C – "Lord, my faith is weak when I do not focus on Your purposes and become more concerned with what others think of me than how you wish me to live. I do not want to be ashamed of You in any way."

T - "Lord, thank You for Your everlasting patience and care as You grow me in my salvation."

S – " Lord, continue to strengthen me in my faith. Keep me from the discouragement of others, whispers of the enemy and self-judgment that is untrue. I want to know and be known for a "Timothy" faith. Amen."

"When my father in his affection for me was trying to turn me from my purpose by arguments and thus weaken my faith, I said to him, 'Do you see this vessel—water pot or whatever it may be? Can it be called by any other name than what it is?' 'No,' he replied. 'So also I cannot call myself by any other name than what I am—a Christian."
~Perpetua~

DIGGING DEEPER:

The words *faithless* and *faithful* are found in 2 Timothy 2:13*. Additional word studies can be done on your own using the Strong's number 4103.

DAY TWO

ON MY KNEES:

Pray. "Father, today, I ask that You open my eyes so that I might truly see the wonderful things of Your Word. The psalmist said that his soul was crushed with longing after Your ordinances at all times. Create a desire like that in me!"

Write. Please write 2 Timothy 1:12-14 in the *"Write!"* section of your study. As you do, prayerfully think about what this verse means to your life. How are you working to retain the sound words of the Bible in your mind and heart?

Read. Take a few minutes and re-read the first chapter of 2 Timothy.

INVESTIGATIVE STUDY
UNDER THE RUG: CROSS REFERENCES

INVESTIGATIVE STUDY

1 Aerial View

2 Streetview

3 Under the Rug

Apply!

Cross-references of *Faith*.

Now you are going to dig even deeper as you search for information about *faith* in other books of the Bible. This information will give you greater comprehension of the *faith* that Paul is emphasizing in 2 Timothy. You will use the Scriptures to learn and understand more about the Scriptures!

Look up these verses and answer the questions for each cross reference. Take notice: often when the word *faith* is used, a description of the gospel is nearby.

Read Hebrews 12:1-2.

What is Jesus' part in our *faith*?

_____

What command are we given regarding our *faith* in verse 2?

_____

Read 1 Peter 5:8-10.

Who is testing our *faith* in this passage?

_____

How are we to react?

_____

According to Mark 11:22, where did Jesus say we should put our *faith*?

_____

_____

What caused Jesus to say that Peter had little *faith* in Matthew 14:31?

_____

_____

What can a strong *faith* accomplish, according to Acts 6:7?

_____

How does Jesus respond when He sees *faith* in Matthew 9:2?

_____

According to Romans 3:28, how is a man saved?

_____

As we research the word *faith*, it is becoming clear that witnessing a sincere *faith* is an encouragement to one's own *faith*. We can encourage others by our walk and others will encourage us by their walk. All glory goes to Jesus as He gives us the strength and reason for our *faith* through His love, suffering and salvation…the Good News of the Gospel!

APPLY!

Today, look back at the name you listed as your Paul on Week 1, Day 2. How could you encourage him/her today? Is there something practical that you could do? Send a handwritten card or purchase a greeting card and send it off in the mail? Unexpectedly take them out to lunch or send flowers? Don't limit yourself to just one of your Paul-like mentors! Make sure to include them in your closing prayers today as well.

A.C.T.S. PRAYER TIME

Turn in your Bible to Titus 2:1-8. Use this passage to pray through your A.C.T.S. Prayer Time prayer model, focusing on how the Lord has provided Christ-like examples in your life. If you feel as though you don't have any really good models to follow, pray for the Lord to provide.

A - *Adoration* _____

C - *Confession* _____

T - *Thanksgiving* _____

S - *Supplication* _____

"True faith is never seen as passive - it is always obedient.
Saving faith is not just believing that Jesus lived and died.
Faith that saves is the confident, continuous confession of total dependence on,
and trust in Jesus Christ to meet the requirements on your behalf
to give you entrance into God's Eternal Kingdom.
It's the surrender of your life in complete trust to Him
to do what you cannot do."
~John MacArthur~

DAY THREE

ON MY KNEES:

Isn't it different to turn off the phone, step away from others and sit in silence? We need to work at finding a quiet time where there aren't any distractions, because we are so easily distracted. Oh, how good it is to sit quietly with the Lord of ages and know that He meets us when we speak with Him. We are privileged to hear, "let's pray now".

Pray. "Here I am, Lord, alone with You. There are not friends, or even enemies here as I settle in to hear from You. I am so used to activity and people that sometimes just being alone with You in Your Word seems odd. Meet me here and help me feel fulfilled by our time together. Make it become a time I cannot do without. I want to feel unsettled…odd, if we don't meet! In Jesus' precious name I pray. Amen."

Write. We cannot encourage you enough concerning how powerful it is to write out Scripture. It seems like such a mundane task, but it has great reward. Continue to persevere in the writing…if you have fallen behind or haven't started, catch up! Today, we will be writing 2 Timothy 1:15.

Read. 2 Timothy, Chapter 1, then, we will begin investigating our last Greek word of the chapter. Don't skip this exercise! The repetition of the reading will help you to recall God's word. You will truly know 2 Timothy inside and out by your study's end.

INVESTIGATIVE STUDY
UNDER THE RUG: KEY WORDS AND WORD STUDIES

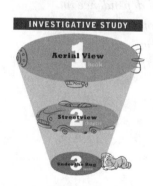

Apply!

We have learned about the Good News, the gospel, of Jesus' redemptive suffering and death on our behalf. We have seen how our faith in the gospel has saved us. Now, Paul weaves the word ***unashamed*** between our first two words of ***gospel*** and ***faith***. Let's get a better understanding of this word so that we might apply it to our faith and how we share it!

PART A: If you were to look up the word ***ashamed*** in Strong's Concordance, you would find that the Strong's number assigned to it in 2 Timothy 1:8, 1:12 and 1:16 is 1870, while 2 Timothy 2:15 uses 422. We will use these numbers to look up the detailed explanation of the Greek words in Part B. Below are the transliteration (the way the word is written in English), the pronunciation, and the basic definition from the Strong's lexicon (dictionary).

1870 *Ashamed. Epaischunomai ep-ahee-skhoo-nom-ahee*; from 1909 (meaning "because of") and 153 (meaning disfigurement, i.e. disgrace); to feel shame for something – be ashamed.

422 *Ashamed. Anepaischuntos au-ep-ah-ee-skhoon-tos*; from one as a negative particle and a presumed derivative of a compilation of 1909 and 153; not ashamed, i.e. by implication irreprehensible – that needeth not to be ashamed.

PART B: If you look up the numbers 1870 and 422 in another Greek lexicon, you can discover further explanations of the meaning of *ashamed* in Greek as seen here:

1. To bring shame upon oneself due to an action
2. To be ashamed of a person, testimony of the Lord (2 Timothy 1:8), another's suffering in the Lord (2 Timothy 1:12), or association with one suffering for the gospel

Synonym: Lupeomai (3076) to be sorry, to invert, withdraw
Antonym: Euphrainomai (2165) to rejoice or to be merry

PART C: As you read these explanations, try to figure out how Paul is using the word *ashamed* in 2 Timothy 1:8, 12 and 16. Remember, he exhorts us **not** to be *ashamed*.

Today, as a part of our investigating the use of ashamed as we see it in 2 Timothy, we are going to look at the both the Greek word, *Epaischunomai*, and it's antonym, *Euphrainomai.*

First, how was this word used in 2 Timothy?

Now, let's look at a couple of places we see examples of the word *ashamed* used in other areas of Scripture.

Read Luke 9:22-26 and answer the following questions:
What happens when a person is *ashamed* of Jesus and His words:

_____

What did Jesus describe in verses 22-25?

_____

What must a man do instead of being *ashamed* of Jesus, according to verse 23?

_____

Read Romans 1:16-17 and answer the following questions:

What does not cause shame?

_____

Why is there no shame?

_____

What is revealed through the gospel?

_____

What does the righteous man live by?

_____

Euphrainomai means to rejoice, make joyful in one's mind or to be glad. What a wonderful attribute to replace that of shame! We are to be joyful and rejoice in our testimony of the Lord, when we see great progress through another's believer's testimony or suffering in the Lord. Obviously, this sounds wrong if we were to think of the suffering only, but we are not rejoicing in the suffering – only the outcome of growth or salvation of souls. We see many occurrences of rejoicing throughout Scriptures. Let's look at a few.

Read Acts 2:25-28.
Who was *glad/rejoiced* in verse 26?

_____

What was the cause of the *rejoicing*?

_____

Was there any shame?

_____

Read Psalm 13:5-6.

_____

What did the psalmist trust in?

_____

What was the cause for his *rejoicing*?

_____

Read 1 Peter 1:3-9.
Who is the cause for great *rejoicing*, according to the summary in verse 8-9?

_____

What did He provide?

_____

For a short time, what might be a part of the *rejoicing*?

_____

Rejoice, again I say rejoice, fellow believers! We have no cause to be ashamed, for our suffering, loss of friends or loneliness is for just a little while. Stand firm in your faith – Jesus has saved you and He is coming back!

APPLY!

Did you know that the WorldNet Dictionary's definition of a Psalm is "any sacred song used to praise the Deity"? The secondary definition in the English dictionary is "one of the 150 lyrical poems and prayers that comprise the Book of Psalms in the Old Testament". Many of today's modern worship songs are from the Book of Psalms. You may not be a songwriter, but you can memorize a Psalm and recite it with passion even if you are not a singer. Memorize 1 Chronicles 16:8-12* over this week and plan to use it to praise the Lord in some way soon.

A.C.T.S. PRAYER TIME

Today, take a moment to read Psalm 40:16 and use it to write in your own prayers.

A - *Adoration* _____

C - *Confession* _____

T - *Thanksgiving* _____

S - *Supplication* _____

"Thy name is excellent, thy glory high, thy condescension wonderful, thy mercy tender. I bless thee for the discoveries, invitations, promises of the gospel for in them is pardon for rebels, liberty for captives, health for the sick, salvation for the lost. I come to thee in thy beloved name of Jesus; re-impress thy image upon my soul; raise me above the smiles and frowns of the world, regarding it as a light thing to be judged by men; may thy approbation be my only aim, thy Word my one rule. Make me to abhor that which grieves thy Holy Spirit, to suspect consolations of a worldly nature, to shun a careless way of life, to reprove evil, to instruct with meekness those who oppose me, to be gentle and patient towards all men, to be not only a professor but an example of the gospel, displaying in every relation, office, and condition its excellency, loveliness and advantages. How little have I illustrated my principles and improved my privileges! How seldom I served my generation! How often have I injured and not recommended my Redeemer! How few are those blessed through me! In many things I have offended, in all come short of thy glory; Pardon my iniquity, for it is great." ("Living for Jesus", The Valley of the Vision)

DIGGING DEEPER:

Why do you think Paul singled out Phygelus and Hermogenes from the "all" who were in Asia?

DAY FOUR

ON MY KNEES:

Pray. "Lord, You say that those who seek You with all their heart will be blessed. I want to want to seek You with all my heart. During these 20 minutes or so, help me to seek You with a steadfast mind. Block out my to-do lists, hedge me in and corral my wandering thoughts. I want to be all Yours."

Write. Write 2 Timothy 1:16-18, praying for a heart to receive all that you will learn today.

Read. 2 Timothy, Chapter 1.

INVESTIGATIVE STUDY
UNDER THE RUG

Apply!

Today, we are going to do something different from our normal routine. As we near the end of our study of 2 Timothy, Chapter 1, it is important to remember why we are studying God's Word.

Our purpose of studying in an in-depth, investigative manner is not so that we gain head knowledge, but so we might know the Lord and His ways in order to deepen our personal, love relationship with Him. We cannot dearly love someone that we do not know. We can learn to love the Lord as He loves us by learning more about His character, attributes, ways, and commands.

You have prepared the foundation to do this by completing the writing of the first chapter of 2 Timothy during the *"Write!"* portion of your Sword Study.

Now, we are going to go to your *"Write!"* section and mark references to God, the Father, the Son and the Holy Spirit. We will mark each person of God in a special way, watching for pronouns for Him as well. Here is how we have done this in the *"Write!"* section:

GOD
the Father

GOD
the Son

GOD
the Holy Spirit

Go ahead and do this now.

Finally, quickly jot a **short,** summary phrase of what you learn about God under the appropriate symbol on the left margin of your *"Write!"* page. For example, in the first verse you would mark "Christ Jesus" and note, "He has apostles" under the triangle symbol with a cross. Do this for each instance that you have marked a reference for God. (Note: it is very helpful to put the verse number at the end of each summary phrase for future reference!) Go ahead and do this now.

Are you amazed at all that the Lord has revealed through His Word about Himself in this short chapter of just 18 verses? Everything points back to His desire for you to know Him. Take a few minutes to answer the following questions about what you learned of God in this first chapter.

God, the Father
What are some of the things that God gives us?

_____

How does God give us His grace?

_____

When did God plan this grace?

_____

God, the Son
What are some of the names by which God's Son is called in these verses?

_____

What promise is found in Jesus?

_____

How long has Jesus been in existence?

_____

What is the most important attribute of Jesus for you, personally, in this chapter?

_____

God, the Holy Spirit
Where does the Holy Spirit reside?

_____

What does He do for us?

_____

How amazing, how wonderful is our God! He is beyond our thoughts and yet He personally reveals Himself to us. He is fathomless, but knowable. He is Creator of all things, but knows the very hairs on my head. He is Holy, Holy, Holy, but a friend to the sinner. He hung on a cross full of sin and shame so I could stand firm unashamed! Praise His name!

APPLY!

Grab a plain piece of paper – or open up an art illustrator program on your computer – and print "My God" in the middle, then begin to write in different style letters some of His attributes using what you learn in 2 Timothy 1.

A.C.T.S. PRAYER TIME

Now, look at your creation and use it as a launching pad for your closing prayer time with the Lord today. If you weren't able to create something immediately, just turn back to your *"Write!"* page and pray through what you wrote down in the short description area.

A - *Adoration*_____

C - *Confession*_____

T - *Thanksgiving*_____

S - *Supplication*_____

"I have had the privilege of preaching the gospel on every continent in most of the countries of the world. And I have found that when I present the simple message of the gospel of Jesus Christ, with authority, quoting from the very Word of God—he takes that message and drives it supernaturally into the human heart."
~Billy Graham~

DAY   FIVE

ON MY KNEES:

Here we are at the end of Week Three of your Sword Study. You may not have been aware of this, but we have been anxiously awaiting your arrival at this point in your study! By God's grace, He leads us to a visual summary that we believe is instrumental in wrapping up your diligent study of a book of the Bible in your Sword Study. We pray that in the future, you will look forward to these summary times as much as we do. Before we jump in, let's begin on our knees for His help in our interpretations.

Pray. "Father give me a clear mind to recall all that I have learned as I review and summarize the first chapter of 2 Timothy. Help me to slow down and not just fill in the blanks. Encourage me with all that You have taught me. Impress me with all You have done in my mind and heart over the last two weeks."

Read. One last time, read Chapter 1. This portion of your letter should look a bit more tattered and worn – in a good way! May the Lord impress on you now the blessings of being so diligent.

INVESTIGATIVE STUDY
1-2-3 CHAPTER 1: SUMMARIZE!

Apply!

Chapter 1 Summary:

Congratulations! You have finished the INVESTIGATIVE STUDY of the first chapter of 2 Timothy. We have a fun way for you to sum up all that you have been learning over the last two weeks.

On the next page, you will see a "Day 10 Diagram". Around the edges of the picture, there are blanks for you to fill out. In the center, the Day 10 Diagram will have a picture that summarizes the chapter. If you have any problems figuring out how to fill in your Day 10 Diagram, talk to a parent; the Parent Guidebook includes the answer key to this diagram.

☐ To begin, look at the top of the Day 10 Diagram. Fill in the chapter number and the title that you created for this chapter.

☐ Next, which verse from the chapter do you think was the "key verse?"

☐ Beside the heart, list the references to any Bible passages that you have hidden in your heart during your study of Chapter 1.

☐ On the right of the page, transfer your key Greek words from this chapter and write a shortened definition of their meanings.

☐ On the bottom of the Diagram page, transfer the most important things that you learned about God through marking the references about Him in your Write! Tab. If you run out of space, continue on the back of your Diagram.

Now, come join in the classroom with teacher Paul and two young "Timothy's" as they learn from this veteran servant of Christ. Paul has vital lessons to share with these young disciples so that they may stand firm for the gospel, but he's not a teacher in ordinary circumstances. First, outline the chains on Paul's ankles, and then, beneath his feet write where he was at when he wrote his final letter to Timothy. To the left of Paul, list the three roles in which this great teacher was still serving God, despite his chains.

Further important instructions are posted on the wall of this classroom. As you studied Chapter 1, what four exhortations did Paul give to his beloved spiritual son (and to us!)? Write them on the "Assignments" list.

Paul also shared some crucial keys to success. On the center whiteboard, list one characteristic that Timothy's **should not** have, as it does not come from God, and then list the three descriptions of the type of spirit God does give. Have you been seeing these last three growing in your life as you know God better?

Moving over to the map on the right side of the wall, label the stars to note Paul and Timothy's locations when Paul wrote 2 Timothy. Refer to your own map from Week 1, Day 4, if needed.

You may have noticed that some students are missing from class, sadly enough. Label each of the three empty chairs with the names of those who deserted Paul. Our prayer is that our young Timothy's will learn their lessons well from their faithful teacher and stand firm in God's power even as times grow more difficult.

Now that you have completed your Diagram, take a few moments to consider the full picture. Be sure to share your thoughts with your family during the **Family Bonfire** time this week.

A . C . T . S .   P R A Y E R   T I M E

Find and read Psalm 66:1-4.

A - "How awesome are Your works, Oh Lord!"

C - "Sometimes I neglect to worship you with my words and actions."

T - "Thank You for displaying Your works so I might see your power visibly."

S - "Help me to sing praises to Your name often and listen to music that proclaims Your praises!"

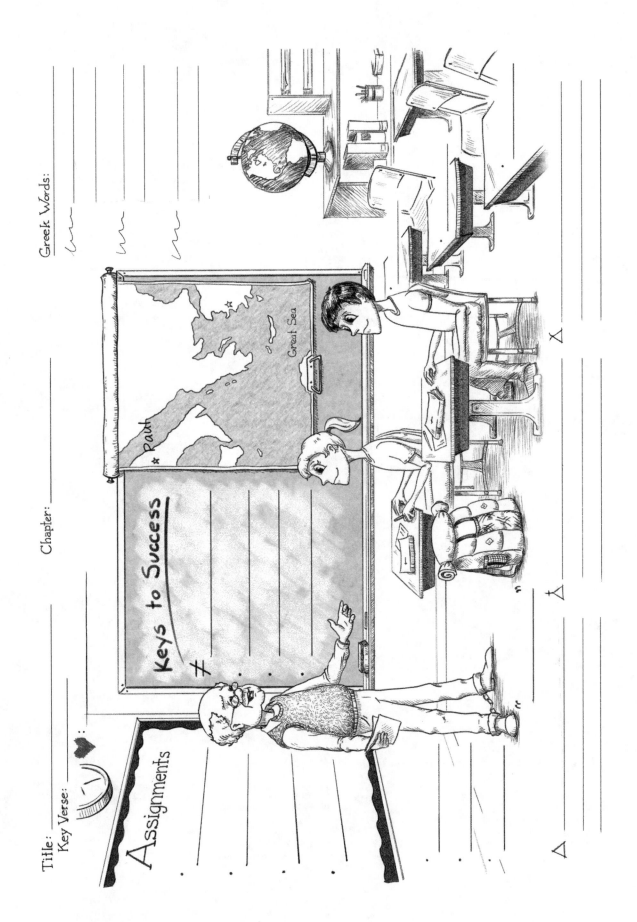

A GOOD SOLDIER:
WILLIAM BOOTH

Scene: A modern-day television studio with chairs for interviewer and interviewee facing each other. A young woman in a business suit sits in one chair as a bearded man in old-fashioned clothing takes the other.

BIBLE BEE TELEVISION (BBTV): *BBTV is proud to present this back-to-the-moment report with General William Booth of the Salvation Army. I'm Bee Diligent, your favorite BBTV host and all-around interview gal, here with five-star General William Booth of the Salvation Army. General, we certainly appreciate your visit with us today.*

GENERAL BOOTH (GB), *speaking with a strong British accent: Glad to be here—although I'm not quite sure how I came. Always good to have a conversation, soldier.*

BBTV: *Soldier? Well, no, not exactly...*

GB: *Why, of course you're a soldier! Scripture says we're in a battle not of this world. If you serve the Lord—and working for BBTV, I know you do—you're a soldier, sure enough.*

BBTV (faltering): *Uhh, sure, whatever you say, Mr. Booth—I mean—General Booth, I mean, Yes, sir!*

GB: *At ease, soldier. Now, about those questions?*

BBTV: *Sir, yes sir! Would you mind telling us a little about your early years, sir? Where were you born?*

GB: *I was born into this world in 1829 in the little village of Sneighton, near Nottingham, England. But at age fifteen, I was born into the next world when I received Christ as my Savior.*

BBTV: *Can you tell us a little more about that second birth?*

GB: *Glad to! I'd gone to a chapel service and, on the way home late at night, found my sin staring me straight in the face. The only way out was to repent and surrender. "God will have all there is of William Booth," I vowed. And I venture to say He did.*

BBTV: *So you started the Salvation Army right after that?*

GB: *No, not then. I did start preaching, though—right there in the streets of Nottingham.*

BBTV: *And how did that go over?*

GB: *Some said I was crazy. Others listened and turned to the Lord. But do you know what troubled me?*

BBTV: *No, sir, I don't.*

GB: *The poor, my good woman, the poor! I'd grown up penniless—still didn't have any money to speak of—and I noticed that whenever I preached, the poor never came forward. So I began going to them.*

BBTV: *Going to them? What do you mean?*

GB: *I took the gospel to the slums. Nottingham had some dreadfully shabby areas, you know. The poor wouldn't come to us, so we took the gospel to them.*

BBTV: *How's that working—I mean, how did that work—for you?*

GB: *They loved the messages and many came to know Christ. But when we went back to the church building, they kicked us out—or at least to the back pew.*

BBTV: *You're kidding! Didn't the church people know what Scripture says about the poor?*

GB: *Only the part about "the poor you will have always with you" (Matt. 26:11, NASB). They wanted the poor to be with us, I guess—as long as they sat in the back.*

BBTV: *What happened next, General?*

GB: God led my wife (I'd married dear Catherine by then) and me to travel and preach. We brought in the poor wherever we went. After all, they needed the message of salvation as much as anyone else. No one spoke for them, and fewer were speaking to them.

BBTV: And did you find acceptance this time?

GB: By the poor, yes. We tried to give them better working conditions, better pay, and of course the glorious news of our Savior. By the church, I'm sad to say, no.

BBTV: You seem like a man of ideas. What came next?

GB: I started a missionary society. I had no better place to reach the heathen than the slums of East London.

BBTV: So what happened?

GB: Failure. Miserable failure—until my new plan.

BBTV: As I said, a man of ideas. So what was the plan?

GB: An army. An army of the cross!

BBTV (musing): I think I know where you're going with this.

GB: Exactly. In 1878, we renamed our mission the Salvation Army. The new plan spread like wildfire.

BBTV: Branding and networking, way back in nineteenth-century England. Who knew?

GB: I beg your pardon?

BBTV: Oh, nothing, sir. So would you count your life a success?

GB: Within ten years, the Salvation Army spread to the United States, Canada, and the Continent—I think you call it Europe. As long as there remained one dark soul without the light of God, I determined to fight—to fight to the very end! Hundreds, thousands, I suppose millions by now came to Christ through our little Army.

BBTV: Sir, your "little army," as you put it, now has more than a million soldiers in 124 countries.

GB (overwhelmed): All I can say, ma'am, is that God is faithful to finish His work. To Him be the glory! (vanishes)

BBTV: Amen and amen. And thank you, General Booth, wherever you are. And to the rest of you—onward, Christian soldiers. To the battle!

DAY ONE

ON MY KNEES:

Welcome to a new week and a new chapter of 2 Timothy! How are you doing? Let's begin this week off correctly, on our knees before our gracious, heavenly Father, Who hears our every plea, praise and thought.

Pray. "God, You are my God. I come before You today in humble adoration, knowing that even though I am undeserving, I am invited, as Your child, to fellowship with You. Speak to me through Your Word today. Make me attuned to Your exhortations for my life."

Write. Please turn to your copy of 2 Timothy and write out 2 Timothy 2:1-4. Prayerfully review the words as you write them, soaking in their meaning.

Read. Read 2 Timothy, Chapter 2.

INVESTIGATIVE STUDY
STREETVIEW: CHAPTER 2

Apply!

For the last two weeks, we have heard from Paul in a loud and clear tone that we are to stand firm in our faith and unashamed of our call to share the gospel and God's Word. For the next two weeks, we turn to the next portion of Paul's letter in Chapter 2. Suddenly, we hear direction after direction in a rapid-fire succession. Hang on as we will systematically break down each of his instructions so that we can take each of them in without being lost in the sheer volume of directives.

We will begin by writing short, summary phrases on each verse of Chapter 2. Due to the length of the chapter, we decided to break the project down over two days.

Remember we are at the STREETVIEW level and you are going to do this to understand the general idea of this second chapter. Our objective is to become familiar with the chapter and this is an effective way to achieve our goal. Try to use only five or six words at the most for your summary phrase, just enough to remind yourself of what you thought the verse was saying. This shouldn't be a laborious task! We have done the first two as examples for you.

Verse 1: <u>Be strong in Jesus</u> _____

Verse 2: <u>Tell others the gospel and how to live</u> _____

Verse 3: _____

Verse 4: _____

Verse 5: _____

Verse 6: _____

Verse 7: _____

Verse 8: _____

Verse 9: _____

Verse 10: _____

Verse 11: _____

Verse 12: _____

Verse 13: _____

Verse 14: _____

APPLY!

Paul tells us to untangle ourselves from the affairs of everyday life. How can we do that? We must ask ourselves what we are doing that distracts us from spending more time as a soldier of Christ.

Write down the commitments of your everyday life on the lines below. Ponder these things. Are you too busy to do things that please your Commanding Officer? Honestly ask yourself if you are in active service for the Lord and if that is what your life shows. This isn't an exercise to condemn or judge, only to evaluate where the Lord may want to convict or guide you. Listen for His voice and be wary if you feel defensive.

_____   _____
_____   _____
_____   _____
_____   _____
_____   _____

A . C . T . S .   P R A Y E R   T I M E

Psalm 50 begins with "The Mighty One, God, the LORD, has spoken". To consider that the Mighty God of the universe speaks to us through His Word is incredibly humbling and encouraging. Begin your time with Adoration for our God who wants us to hear His voice. Confess those times when you are tempted not to listen. Thank Him for His faithfulness. Ask Him to open your ears so that You won't miss anything He is saying to you as you continue to study 2 Timothy.

A - *Adoration* _____

C - *Confession* _____

T - *Thanksgiving* _____

S - *Supplication* _____

"He who has the Holy Spirit in his heart and the Scriptures in his hands has all he needs."
~Alexander Maclaren~

D A Y   T W O

ON MY KNEES:

Pray. "Lord, I see Your lovingkindness in my days and Your song is with me at night. How great are Your promises! They speak to my heart because You know my thoughts. Multiply my joy and blessings as I prepare to spend time in Your Word today."

Write. 2 Timothy 2:5-7

Read. Diligently read 2 Timothy, Chapter 2 again today.

INVESTIGATIVE STUDY
STREETVIEW: CHAPTER 2

Apply!

Are you ready to finish up your short, summary phrases for the last 12 verses of the chapter? Regardless, here we go! Keep up the great work!

Verse 15: _____

Verse 16: _____

Verse 17: _____

Verse 18: _____

Verse 19: _____

Verse 20: _____

Verse 21: _____

Verse 22: _____

Verse 23: _____

Verse 24: _____

Verse 25: _____

Verse 26: _____

Before we wrap up our time in the Word today, take a few minutes to write down any new people that Paul introduces in Chapter 2. On the lines below, write down the names or references to people that Paul mentions in these last verses. Next to their name include a short observation concerning them. (Do not include any of the Trinity at this time.)

Person(s)   Observation
_____   _____
_____   _____

Do not be discouraged young Timothy! Be strong in all that you are learning from Paul. Turn to 1 Timothy 1:15-19* to hear his personal summary of his life. Summarize how this encourages you in your walk today. _____
_____
_____
_____

APPLY!

Do you play any sports or have a favorite board game? In the first column of lines below write the name of the sport or game on the first line, and then on the following lines, write top five rules of the game.

_____   _____
1. _____   1. _____
2. _____   2. _____
3. _____   3. _____
4. _____   4. _____
5. _____   5. _____

Do you ever wonder why we don't fuss about the rules of a game, but struggle so with the "rules" we feel God gives us to live well? What happens when you break one of the rules? Now, in the second column of lines, write "Christian Life" on the first line and then write in some of the rules that you think God has for your life. Feel free to use some of the ones Paul shares in 2 Timothy, Chapter 2. Why is it that it is easier to obey Milton Bradley or another game company than obeying our loving, Heavenly Father? Evaluate your own thoughts and motives against the Word, and continue.

A.C.T.S. PRAYER TIME

According to 2 Timothy 2:19, "The Lord knows who are His". Not only does our Mighty God of the universe speak to us through His Word but also He knows us intimately. Psalm 139 adds, "O LORD, you have searched me and known me! You know when I sit down and when I rise up; you discern my thoughts from afar." As you enter into your time of adoration, praise God for being a personal God who knows all about you. In your time of supplication, pray along with Paul that you "May know him, and the power of his resurrection, and the fellowship of his sufferings, being made conformable unto his death". (Philippians 3:10).

A - *Adoration*_____

C - *Confession*_____

T - *Thanksgiving*_____

S - *Supplication*_____

"God's mind is revealed in Scripture, but we can see nothing
without the spectacles of the Holy Ghost."
~Thomas Manton~

DIGGING DEEPER

According to 2 Timothy 2:18, men will go astray from the truth. Investigate Billy Graham and Charles Templeton at www.reclaimingthemind.com to see what different stances on Scripture can do to a person's life.

DAY THREE

ON MY KNEES:

What a privilege we have been given to enter freely into the presence of the Holy God of the Universe! Let's go to him now.

Pray. "O God, revive the joy of my salvation, and sustain in me a willing spirit because I want to be used by You. I am here in body, but want to give You all my attention, so please help me stay focused today!"

Write. 2 Timothy 2:8-10

Read. Do you know what we are going to ask? Correct! Please read Chapter 2 of 2 Timothy.

INVESTIGATIVE STUDY
STREETVIEW: INTERVIEWING THE CHAPTER

Apply!

Thus far, during your overview of Chapter 2, you may have noticed that there are quite a few exhortations or "charges" that Paul gives Timothy. An easy way to pick these out of the text is by looking for verbs. Today, we will do just that. In addition, we will document any lists that correspond with the commands. By the time we are finished we will have what is equivalent to a sentence diagram of our chapter, or an outline of sorts! For now, ignore the "Definitions" column; we will return tomorrow to focus on that portion of the chart. Follow our example…

Exhortations of 2 Timothy – Chapter 2

	Exhortation (Verb)	What	Verse	Definition
I.	Be Strong/Strengthened		1	
	a.	in Jesus' grace		
	b.	in what Paul said		
II.	Entrust/Commit	Paul's words to faithful men	2	
III.			3	
IV.			7	
V.		Jesus Christ	8	
	a.			
	b.			
VI.		of these things	14	
	a.		vs. 11-13	
	b.			
	c.			
	d.			
VII.			14	
VIII.		as workman	15	
	a.			
	b.			
	c.			
	d.			
IX.			19	
X.			22	
XI.		from a pure heart	22	
	a.			
	b.			
	c.			
	d.			
XII.			23	
XIII.	Be a servant who…		vs. 24-25	
	a.			
	b.			
	c.			
	d.			
	e.			

APPLY!

*Note: If you're having trouble solving the puzzle, it may help to look at various Bible versions.

Across

3. Be a/an _____ workman
4. Paul's words to faithful men
8. Be ____ in Jesus' grace
9. Hardships
10. … to what I say!

Down

1. Youthful lusts/desires/passions
2. Jesus Christ
5. One who does not quarrel, is kind, teaches and corrections
6. Elect/chosen of their salvation
7. From a pure heart

A.C.T.S. PRAYER TIME

He has risen, indeed! His Word continues to go out today – we are a testimony to this fact as we study Paul's words written from a prison in the AD 60's. His Word is eternal, never returns void and is sharper than a two- edged sword.

A - "You are stronger, sin has been broken. You have saved me. It is written, Christ has risen and I have every reason to rejoice!"

C - "Lord, I want You to be my all and yet, I know I do not live that way. Forgive me for getting lost in myself and the activity of the temporal."

T – "Thank You for Your patience in training, teaching and disciplining me in Your mercy and lovingkindness."

S – "Draw me one step closer to You and help me to see more of the eternal than the temporal today. Prick my heart and mind throughout the day to see the evidences of Your hand. Jesus, use Your Word today to empower us to walk in Your ways. Open my eyes as I leave this time with You."

"'Not called!' did you say? 'Not heard the call,' I think you should say. Put your ear down to the Bible, and hear him bid you go and pull sinners out of the fire of sin. Put your ear down to the burdened, agonized heart of humanity, and listen to its pitiful wail for help. Go stand by the gates of hell, and hear the damned entreat you to go to their father's house and bid their brothers and sisters, and servants and masters not to come there. And then look Christ in the face, whose mercy you have professed to obey, and tell him whether you will join heart and soul and body and circumstances in the march to publish his mercy to the world."
~William Booth!~

DAY FOUR

INVESTIGATIVE STUDY
STREETVIEW: CHAPTER 2

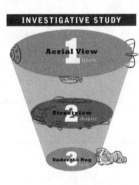

Apply!

As we dissected Chapter 2 yesterday, we could imagine an audible voice of increased urgency in how Paul began to rattle off instruction after instruction. We would do well to remember that he was sitting in a dark, dank prison cell knowing that his death was very near. He was not sitting at a beautiful, cherry desk with lovely parchment scattered about, holding an elegant feather pen.

Our picture of Paul as passionate, energized, pillar of faith speaking in front of a large audience in a tidy synagogue has quickly faded. We find ourselves hearing from a now aged, battered, suffering prisoner, who is crying out from the depths of a prison pit with urgency. He is going to be gone soon. He has wisdom. He wants a last word. He wants to charge the younger in the faith to pick up the torch, and not to just limply catch it, but to grab it and HOLD IT HIGH! (Even if all his friends in the faith are deserting in shame!)

Dear beloved, faithful student of the Word today, you are Paul's audience. Hear Your heavenly Father's holy call to you!

Turn your attention back to the list of verbs we gathered on our chart. Today, we will define them using a dictionary; ideally, it would be best to use a Bible dictionary. Look up each verb of exhortation, read the definition and then create your own paraphrased definition in the far right column marked "definitions" on your "Exhortations of 2 Timothy Chart" from yesterday. Don't leave out the definitions of the examples we provided.

APPLY!

Do you remember the "Apply" exercise on rules? After today's dictionary work on Paul's commands, which directive do you find easiest to follow? _____
_____ Is there an exhortation that you find hard to swallow and difficult to obey? Write it out here: _____ Why is it difficult for you? _____ Pray for God's strength, and purpose to overcome your difficulty on this one with Him.

A.C.T.S. PRAYER TIME

"How good it is to know, Lord, that You are faithful even when I am faithless. What a comfort! What peace these words give me for the times when I question. You are bigger and Your ways higher than mine. I am so glad that everything does not depend on what I know and understand. Help me grow in my faith so that I might glorify You. Help me not measure how much I don't know, but to rejoice in drawing closer to You and the deepening of our relationship. Thank you for meeting me in Your Scriptures today. "

A - *Adoration*_____

C - *Confession*_____

T - *Thanksgiving*_____

S - *Supplication*_____

"You must pray with all your might. That does not mean saying your prayers, or sitting gazing about in church or chapel with eyes wide open while someone else says them for you. It means fervent, effectual, untiring wrestling with God. This kind of prayer be sure the devil and the world and your own indolent, unbelieving nature will oppose. They will pour water on this flame."
~William Booth~

D A Y   F I V E

O N   M Y   K N E E S :

We have come to another end of a week. You are gaining wisdom – God's wisdom, as you commit yourself to the study of His Word. Keep up the great work! Stay the course!

Pray. "Lord, I want to remember Your teachings and keep Your commands. You promise that they will add to the length of my days, years to my life and give me peace. Make the words I study today deeply adhere to my heart and change my daily walk."

Write. Today, as you write 2 Timothy 2:14-15 behind the *"Write!"* tab of your Sword Study, prayerfully consider what the Lord might be saying to you through these verses today.

Read. Find a sibling. Call a grandparent. Dial a friend. Together, read 2 Timothy 2 together. Make the time short, just enough to read with one another and maybe even pray – and then carry on with your study.

I N V E S T I G A T I V E   S T U D Y
STREETVIEW: CHAPTER 2

Suddenly, three types of people show up on the pages of Paul's letter; a soldier, athlete and farmer. How odd. This isn't a part of Paul's normal pattern, so it warrants a closer look.

What is the first thing you think of when you think of a soldier? Write it here:

_____

What is the first thing you think of when you think of an athlete? Write it here:

_____

What is the first thing you think of when you think of a farmer? Write it here:

_____

Paul used these analogies to help us better understand how to live a life for Christ. For the next several days, we will look at each one to understand how they can contribute to our understanding.

The Soldier

Definition: A brave warrior; a person of military experience and skill, or a person of distinguished valor; used by way of emphasis or distinction. [2]

Paul's call to be like soldiers is not a new charge to the ears of his readers. We will see he has used it in his other letters and messages to the believers of the churches. As Christ's soldiers, what are we to do, according to each of the following exhortations:

Ephesians 6:10-12

_____

1 Timothy 6:12

_____

Here are a few other passages that speak to being a soldier or depending on our Master for the strength to fight the battle. Find the passages and answer the questions that follow.

What attributes about our God do you find in Psalm 144:1-4 that would help us in the battle?

_____

Who is our strength and what should we do for Him according to Psalm 81:1?

_____

What in Psalm 37:38 should be a comfort to us as soldiers for the Lord?

_____

Where is the kingdom that we fight for, according to John 18:36?

_____

In summary, Paul calls us to be good soldiers who are not distracted by our daily cares or worldly temptations, but who are on call at all times and seek to please our Commander in Chief, not our fellow enlistees or the enemy. Next time we come together, we will evaluate his use of a "man of masteries", the athlete.

APPLY!

Whether your artistic skills are at a stick figure or Pixar level, draw a person below. Using Ephesians 6:10-18*, dress him or her in the armor (labeled) that will spiritually prepare him for battle. Memorization of this passage is highly recommended!

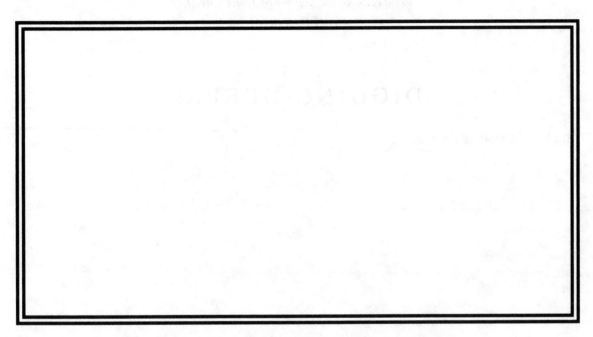

A.C.T.S. PRAYER TIME

Thank you, Lord, for the words of 2 Timothy 2:15; they are like an encouragement sent directly to me as I am trying to be diligent in how I handle Your Word by studying it daily in my Sword Study. From before time You wrote these words and they seem to be for such a time as this for me. I love Your confirmation of Your work in me.

A - *Adoration* _____

C - *Confession* _____

T - *Thanksgiving* _____

S - *Supplication* _____

"Every professing Christian is the soldier of Christ. He is bound ... to fight Christ's battle against sin, the world and the devil. The man that does not do this breaks his vow. He is a spiritual defaulter. He does not fulfill the engagements made for him. The man that does not do this is practically renouncing his Christianity. The very fact that he belongs to a church, attends a Christian place of worship, and calls himself a Christian, is a public declaration that he desires to be reckoned a soldier of Jesus Christ."

~ J.C. Ryle~

DIGGING DEEPER

Study the history of the canon.

HONOR BOUND: Eric Liddell

"He who honors Him, He will honor."

So read the torn scrap of paper in Eric Liddell's pocket. The trainer for Scotland's Olympic runners had given it to him that morning.

Weeks earlier, Eric made a decision not to run in his usual race, the 100-meter. The 1922 Paris Olympic Committee had scheduled that race to take place on a Sunday. But Eric considered Sundays holy days. Participating in the race would dishonor the God he loved. Instead, Eric requested a spot in the more exhausting 400-meter run.

Race day had arrived. Could he do it?

Head thrown back and feet pounding down the track, he rounded the final turn of the 400-meter. But where were the rest of the runners? Eric crossed the finish line—alone.

That day, Eric Liddell set a new world record and won a gold medal. More than that, he won the respect of a watching world. God had honored a young man's choice.

Choices and Changes

In the years that followed, Eric faced other important choices. The next year, instead of pursuing fame or finances, he returned to North China to continue his parents' missionary work.

By that time, the Japanese invasion of China made missionary life dangerous. But Eric chose to marry a young woman also called to serve in missions. Together, the two pursued their work in China, soon adding three daughters to their family.

Violence escalated. When a wounded Chinese soldier needed

help, Eric walked more than twenty miles to bring him to a mission hospital. His ministry looked different now, but it came from the same heart.

Before long, the British government asked all missionaries to leave China. Eric sent his family to Canada. He chose to stay and carry out his missionary commitment. His life would continue to honor God.

Soon, the Japanese forced Eric and about 1800 others from all sorts of backgrounds into a crowded concentration camp. How could he honor God here?

Final Surrender

God made a way. Eric became the unofficial camp leader, making sure his fellow prisoners had fresh food, water, and medical supplies. He took responsibility in other areas, too, doing the chores no one else wanted.

Eric did his best to serve his fellow prisoners. When a woman whom no one respected needed a bookshelf, he built her one. Later, she said Eric was the only person who did something nice for her without asking anything in return. Eric helped the elderly, taught Bible classes, organized games, and taught science to the camp children. He also spent hours discipling the youth, who knew him as kind, fair, and genuine.

"Eric so lived in the Word," said Meredith Helsby (a fellow missionary also interned at the camp) "that when he spoke it was with a sincerity that made you feel he was speaking directly to you."

More choices lay ahead. The British government negotiated a prisoner exchange, which meant Eric could leave the camp at last. But he refused to leave, insisting a pregnant woman go in his place. Before long, he became ill and had to enter the camp hospital. Even in weakness, he continued to teach, sing, and honor God.

Eric Liddell died of a massive brain tumor on February 21, 1945. His last words, "Surrender. Surren. . ." reflect the choices he made and the life he lived—fully surrendered, fully devoted to the God he chose to honor in life and in death.

D A Y   O N E

ON MY KNEES:

Onward, Christian soldier - continue marching in the battle! Welcome back to your study of 2 Timothy. We pray that you are coming with a mindset ready to learn more of the Lord and His ways. Begin with prayer before we dig in again.

Pray. "Lord, I want to be alert and ready for Your message to me through what I will be studying. Help me not to rush or simply methodically go through the motions of Bible study today. Use Your precepts to sever the areas of complacency in me."

Write. 2 Timothy 2:16-18 are the verses that we're going to write today. Please think about what you are writing. Here we find the result of an uncontrolled tongue. Allow the Lord to speak to you if there is any truth of these things in your life. He is able to help you overcome any sin.

Read. Open your Word of God and purposefully read Chapter 2 of 2 Timothy.

INVESTIGATIVE STUDY
STREETVIEW: CHAPTER 2

Apply!

As we finished up last week in 2 Timothy, we saw how Paul used the example of a soldier to spur Timothy on in the spiritual battle of the gospel. Today, we look at his second example: the athlete.

The Athlete ("man of masteries" in KJV)

Definition: Anyone trained to contend in exercises requiring great physical agility and strength; one who has great activity and strength; a champion. [3]

Read the following passages and note what you learn about a good athlete or racer.

1 Corinthians 9:24

_____

1 Timothy 1:15-19*

_____

Hebrews 12:1-2

_____

Have you ever seen athletes go all-out, amaze an audience and raise their hands in victory – only to hang their heads in defeat when an official waves a flag of disqualification? How can it be? They practiced for months, struggled for every inch of the event, but then they broke a rule. May this not be true of us! Run well...better yet, run right. The Word of God is filled with instructions on how to run right. We study to know Him more. The more we know Him, the more we love Him. The more we love Him the more we want to please Him. We show Him our love by obeying His Word. We run well by obeying God's Word. This is great logic!

APPLY!

Research a famous Christian athlete or master and read a book or watch a DVD about his or her life. Pay particular attention to his or her training regimen. The examples Paul is using to give us a picture of how to live our lives are beginning to sound like work. Hmmm...

A.C.T.S. PRAYER TIME

"Oh, Lord, the point of the verses I wrote were very clear. I need to watch my conversations and avoid worldly or pointless discussions. This is not an easy charge. Please give me the discernment and perseverance to obey this exhortation from Paul's words. Help me to train and work on this area of discipline with Your power."

A - *Adoration*_____

C - *Confession*_____

T - *Thanksgiving*_____

S - *Supplication*_____

"You are the light of the world. A city on a hill cannot be hidden.
Neither do people light a lamp and put it under a bowl.
Instead they put it on its stand, and it gives light to everyone in the house.
In the same way, let your light shine before men,
that they may see your good deeds and praise your Father in heaven."
~ Matthew 5:14-16 NIV ~

D A Y   T W O

ON MY KNEES:

Are you ready and eager to start, or slow and dragging as you arrive today? Either way, the Lord has been patiently waiting without demanding your time. With gentle summons, He calls you to join Him. Humbly go to your knees and bow before Your God in prayer.

Pray. "Heavenly Father, how true that You did not force me to come here or require a set time that I must stay. Forgive me when I don't rush here with excitement. Give me a heart that wants to stay longer. Help me to long for Your presence more than anything else in this world."

Write. Please open up to the *"Write!"* section of your Sword Study. Today, let's write 2 Timothy 2:19-20. As you do, rejoice in the fact that the Lord recognizes you! You are very blessed.

Read. Today, read both Chapter 1 and 2 of 2 Timothy.

INVESTIGATIVE STUDY
UNDER THE RUG: WORD STUDIES

Apply!

Finally, we come to the profession of a farmer. As some people think about farming, a cute red barn, fluffy sheep and a cow named Betsy come to mind. Oh, how cute, let's go pet some kittens! For others, the sweat immediately begins to appear on their brows as they think of baling hay, pulling a row of weeds or carrying a bucket of water to a flock of smelly chickens, all in 100 degrees or a foot of snow. Where's the storybook? Paul's picture is much closer to the latter.

The Farmer/Husbandman
Definition: One who is devoted to the tillage of the soil; one who cultivates a farm; an agriculturist. [4]

Read the following passages and note what you learn about farmers.

Proverbs 24:30-34 _____

Proverbs 28:19 _____

James 5:7-8 _____

The hard-working farmer does not see the fruits of his labor instantly, but has to wait patiently for the process of growth. Oftentimes a farmer's diligent efforts do not guarantee a good return on his investment, yet the call to continue the work in and out of season, year after year remains. The Greek word used here for hard-working, *kopiao*, meant "to toil intensely; to sweat and stain to the point of exhaustion." The farmer is known for his early starting and late quitting times. "He endures the cold, the heat, the rain, and the drought. He plows the soil whether it is hard or loose. He does not wait for his own convenience, because the seasons do not wait for him. When the time comes to plant, he must plant; when the weeds appear, he must remove them; and when the crop is mature, he must harvest it. What drives the man to such hard toil is the harvest." [5]

Ultimately, why should the hard worker work? Use Colossians 3:22-24* to give your response on the lines below: _____

_____

Do you have a fuller picture of why Paul may have used these three examples for us to better relate to suffering for Christ and sharing His gospel to others? Do you see that just as the soldier wins freedom, the runner a prize and the farmer the first fruits of the fields, that we will be given a crown far above earthly worth in our pursuits for Christ? We are blessed indeed!

APPLY!

Take a trip to a nearby nursery or the garden department of a local store. Purchase a small seed packet and follow the directions for planting the seeds. Let's see how easy this farming profession really is over the next couple of weeks. Follow the rules of care carefully!

A.C.T.S. PRAYER TIME

Praise the Lord today as the Resurrection and the Life. Only our God, no other, has power over death and the grave. Jesus is the risen Savior! He gives those who trust in His name eternal life. Becoming consumed with our problems and circumstances is very easy. We see them as insurmountable and forget the power we have over them through God. Enter into your time of prayer praising our all-powerful God!

A - *Adoration* _____

C - *Confession* _____

T - *Thanksgiving* _____

S - *Supplication* _____

DIGGING DEEPER

The word, **Lord**, appears 16 times in the book of 2 Timothy and the same word is used more than 6,600 times throughout the Scriptures. There is little doubt that the Word of God has woven through its pages the Lord's name, attributes, commands and causes for fear and rejoicing. His name is a core thread, because the Scripture is surely His story. Let's find out the Greek word and its meaning, then we'll look at a few cross references. There will be plenty more possibilities if you would like to investigate more on your own!

Word Study:

PART A: If you were to look up the word **Lord** in Strong's Concordance, you would find that the Strong's number assigned to it in every instance in 2 Timothy is 2962. We will use this number to look up the detailed explanation of the Greek word in Part B. Below is the trans-literation (the way the word is written in English), the pronunciation, and the basic definition from the Strong's lexicon (dictionary).

2962. *Kurios. koo-ree-os,* supreme in authority, i.e. (as a noun) controller. Implies respectful title as Mr. – Sir, master, God.

PART B: If you look up the number 2962 in another Greek lexicon, you can discover further explanation of the meaning of **Lord** in Greek as seen here:

1. General

    a. Possessor, owner, master of property.
    b. Supreme lord, sovereign, e.g., Roman emperor

2. Spoken of God and Christ

    a. Of God as supreme Lord and sovereign of universe (Jehovah in Hebrew)
    b. Of the Lord Jesus Christ

        i. Master, Teacher, Rabbi
        ii. Lord of gospel. Lord over all things to the church.

PART C: Paul uses the definition under "B. 2" in each instance found in 2 Timothy. As you mark the text you will be able to determine whether he is speaking of the Father or Son.

Look up the following passages and then write what you learn about God and answer the additional investigative questions that follow each passage.

Genesis 22:14 _____

What attribute of the *Lord* is highlighted in this passage? _____

Joshua 3:13 _____

What descriptive phrase is used for the *Lord* in this passage? _____

Psalm 8 _____

What amazes the psalmist most in this passage? _____

Psalm 83:18 _____

What is God over in this passage? _____

Who is higher than Him? _____

Isaiah 12:2 _____

What attribute of the *Lord* is highlighted in this passage? _____

Finish the three sentences with what the psalmist says the *Lord* is to us.

The *Lord* is my _____, my _____, and my _____

Isaiah 26:4 _____

What attribute of the *Lord* is highlighted in this passage? _____

Romans 4:8 _____

What power does God have in regards to sin according to this passage? _____

_____

Luke 1:16-17 _____

What prepares people for the *Lord* in this passage? _____

D A Y   T H R E E

INVESTIGATIVE STUDY
UNDER THE RUG: CROSS REFERENCES

Apply!

Today, you are going to look for key words. Remember, key words are repeated words or words that contribute to the central meaning of the text. Carefully read Chapter 2 and mark the key words as you read. You can be creative in how you mark the words. For example, you may want to circle each occurrence of "Paul" and place a "P" above them. Do whatever helps you to visually see the key words jump out of the text. After you mark all of your key words, list them here: _____

_____

_____

_____

Once again, key words are subjective, so don't feel as though you have failed if you didn't choose the word or words that we chose to highlight. Today, we are simply going to read through the word study of "suffer" in preparation for looking at the word within 2 Timothy and other cross references.

Word Study:
PART A: The Strong's Concordance number for *suffer* is 3958. We are also going to look up the word *sufferings*; the Strong's number assigned to it is 3804. Below are the transliterations, their pronunciations, and the basic definitions according to Strong's dictionary:

3804. *Sufferings. Pathema. path'-ay-mah*, something undergone, i.e. hardship or pain; an emotion or influence. The sufferings of a Christian are so called because they endured for the sake of Christ and in conformity to His suffering.

3958. *Suffer.* *Pascho* *pas'-kho*, including the forms patho *path'-o*, and pentho *pen'tho*, verb; to experience a sensation or impression (usually painful):--feel, passion, suffer, vex.

PART B: If you were to look up the numbers 3958 and 3804 in another Greek dictionary, you would discover further explanations of the meanings of *suffer* and *sufferings* in Greek, as listed below:

3804. Sufferings

    1) that which one suffers or has suffered

        a) externally, a suffering, misfortune, calamity, evil, affliction

        - of the sufferings of Christ

        - also the afflictions which Christians must undergo on behalf of the same cause which Christ patiently endured

        b) of an inward state, an affliction, passion

    2) an enduring, undergoing, suffering

3958. Suffer, be vexed

    1) to be affected or have been affected, to feel, have a sensible experience, to undergo

        a) in a good sense, to be well off, in good case

        b) in a bad sense, to suffer sadly, be in a bad plight

PART C. As you read through those explanations, replace the word with the definition to better understand Paul's use of the word *suffer* in 2 Timothy.

APPLY!

As you read through the definitions of *suffer* and *suffering*, did you notice that suffering does not always involve physical duress? Various types of hardships and persecutions cause suffering. Paul has pointed out physical circumstances, but he has also highlighted, significantly, the hardship that comes from watching others walk from the faith or desert us. God is a people person. We are people persons, created to be relational because of His value for relationship. Why is desertion difficult?

_____

Has this ever happened to you? _____ If it has, how did it make you feel?

_____ There are many books these days that discuss people, especially youth, walking away from their faith. Paul tells us how to combat any desires to abandon our faith in ourselves, and how help others who struggle with the same. How would you summarize his instruction from what you have learned so far?

How to combat desires to desert in myself: _____

_____

How to help others: _____

_____

A.C.T.S. PRAYER TIME

We worship the Lord Jesus, as the One and only God, highly exalted and bestowed with the name above every name, at which every knee will bow, both those in heaven and on earth. We can enter our time of prayer bowing our knee in worship as we confess Jesus as our Lord. What a privilege!

A - *Adoration* _____

C - *Confession* _____

T - *Thanksgiving* _____

S - *Supplication* _____

DIGGING DEEPER

Look up the following passages, then write what you learn about Jesus, and answer the additional investigative questions that follow each passage.

Jesus is our Master...Teacher...Rabbi

Matthew 17:4-5 _____

What did God command the disciples to do regarding Jesus in this passage?

_____

John 13:13-14 _____

What was Jesus called in each of these passages?

John 1:38 _____

John 20:16 _____

Luke 7:40 _____

Revelation 17:14 _____

Jesus is the Lord of the gospel...

Romans 10:12-13 _____

Although the word *gospel* is not in this passage, how is the gospel described in this verse?

_____

D A Y   F O U R

ON MY KNEES:

Pray. "Lord, I am alert, and ready to stand firm, be strong and wait on You. Show me Your ways and thoughts as I dig into 2 Timothy today."

Write. As you write 2 Timothy 2:24-26, stop and read Paul's words out loud. These words state that how you speak is important and used in mighty ways. Hear the exhortation of this servant of the Lord. Ponder these things as you write His Word on your page and in your heart today.

Read. As we near the end of our study of 2 Timothy, Chapter 2, once again turn your focus to the reason we study the Word of God...to know Him!

INVESTIGATIVE STUDY
UNDER THE RUG: CROSS REFERENCES

When we were last together, we studied the Greek meaning and definition of the word *suffer* or *suffering*. First, we will look at the various instances that Paul used *suffer* in 2 Timothy and then we will see how it is used in other Scriptures.*

2 Timothy 1:8

What is worth *suffering* for in this passage?

_____

What does Paul ask Timothy to do about *suffering*?

_____

2 Timothy 1:12

Why is Paul *suffering* in this passage?

_____

Why is he not ashamed to *suffer* for these things?

_____

2 Timothy 2:3

What is paired with *suffering* in this passage?

_____

Who is used as an example of *suffering* in this passage?

_____

2 Timothy 2:9
What word is paired with *suffering* in this passage?

_____

How far did Paul's *suffering* go in this passage?

_____

2 Timothy 3:10-11
Who had *suffered* in this passage?

_____

Who followed in *suffering*?

_____

Note what you learn about *suffering* in Philippians 1:27-30*:

_____

_____

According to Luke 24:46-47, who *suffered* and why?

_____

What does 2 Corinthians 1:4-6 tell us about *suffering*?

_____

What do you learn about *suffering* in 1 Peter 2:20?

_____

*Those who use the ESV may need to refer to another translation for the cross references to suffer related to hardship and Paul's example.

APPLY!

"Sticks and stones will break your bones, but words will never hurt you." Who wrote that?! It is a farce. As you wrote today's Scripture, you learned that how we control our tongues is extremely important to the Lord. Take a look at James 1:19-20. Watch for times today that you can choose to not speak or return an unkind word. (What you say inside your head counts, too!)

A.C.T.S. PRAYER TIME

We praise You God, who had mercy on Paul and Epaphroditus, and who has had mercy on us. Instead of letting us be separated from You for eternity, You sent Your Son to die in our place so we could know You as Father. Forgive us when we do not give others mercy when we have received so much mercy every day from You. Oh, that we might understand the depths of Your mercy!

117

A - *Adoration* _____

C - *Confession* _____

T - *Thanksgiving* _____

S - *Supplication* _____

DIGGING DEEPER

If you have additional time and energy, it would be so beneficial for you to do a word study on the word *hardship*.

Your *"Write!"* section now has Chapter 2 written within the pages and you have your foundation prepared to mark all of the references to God, the Father, the Son and the Holy Spirit. As a quick reminder, here are the symbols that we will use for each reference:

GOD
the Father

GOD
the Son

GOD
the Holy Spirit

Read through your copy of 2 Timothy 2 and mark each reference to God now.

Next, fill in your *short*, summary phrases of what you learn about God under the appropriate symbol on the left margin of your *"Write!"* page.

Have you gleaned new reasons to honor and glorify your Lord? Have you been reminded of where you need to focus your praise and prayers? Lastly, close your time of study by answering the following questions about what you learned of God in 2 Timothy 2.

God, the Father
How are we to present ourselves to the Father?

_____

What seals the firm foundation of God?

_____

God, the Son
Who is one of Jesus' forefathers?

_____

What is the result of denying Jesus?

_____

DAY FIVE

ON MY KNEES:

See the ant? Watch her ways! We find these words in Proverbs 6:6. You are not a sluggard, my friend! Today marks the half-way mark of our Sword Study. You are accomplishing much, fellow sojourner! Continue your course because the Lord is well-pleased with the diligent, and you are among His faithful. Begin with prayer before starting your summary day of 2 Timothy, Chapter 2.

Pray. "Lift up Your countenance upon me Lord. Put the gladness in my heart that only You can give as I spend time at Your feet. I want the peace you promise through the study of Your Word."

Read. Quietly read 2 Timothy, Chapter 2.

INVESTIGATIVE STUDY
1-2-3 CHAPTER 2: SUMMARIZE!

INVESTIGATIVE STUDY

1 Aerial View *book*

2 Streetview *chapter*

3 Under the Rug

Apply!

Chapter 2 Summary:

Have you been looking forward to this day throughout the week? Remember, if you have any problems figuring out how to fill in your *Day 10 Diagram*, talk to a parent; the Parent Guidebook includes the key to this diagram.

☐ To begin, look at the top of the *Day 10 Diagram*. Fill in the chapter number and the title that you created for this chapter.

☐ Next, which verse from the chapter do you think was the "key verse?"

☐ Beside the heart, list the references to any Bible passages you have hidden in your heart during your study of Chapter 2.

☐ On the right of the page, transfer your key Greek words from this chapter and write a shortened definition of their meanings.

☐ On the bottom of the *Diagram* page, transfer the most important things that you learned about God through marking the references about Him in your Write! Section. If you run out of space, continue on the back side of your Diagram.

It's time for these young Timothy's to take their lessons from the classroom and apply them during some real-life training. Paul warns them that it won't be easy, but gives them three great models to understand more about what it means to suffer unashamedly for Christ.

Begin by labeling each of the three examples that Paul gives in Chapter 2 above each corresponding person in the Diagram.

As always, Paul sets an example for the young disciples. In our Diagram, he is wearing the armor of God as a faithful soldier for Christ. List each piece of the armor that God tells us to wear and what each piece represents in Ephesians 6:10-18 to the left of Paul. Write the lesson that every soldier must learn in the blank beneath Paul.

Our young lady has been training hard as an athlete, because she is striving to win the prize. It's tiring and sometimes painful to keep persevering, but she knows that she must press on. Note the other lesson that she has learned as an athlete beneath her weary feet.

The young man has sweated through many hours of work as a farmer, but is beginning to taste satisfaction from his toil. Label what keeps every farmer going through the early mornings and late evenings of hard physical labor beneath this Timothy's feet.

While we can learn what it means to walk as a disciple of Christ from each of these examples, Paul also included several truths in Chapter 2 that every follower of Jesus would do well to remember when suffering comes. Fill in the "IF/THEN" chart with the promises that Paul shared with us.

Now that you have completed your Diagram, take a few moments to consider the full picture. Be sure to share your thoughts with your family during the **Family Bonfire** time this week.

A . C . T . S . P R A Y E R T I M E

"Lord, this is what I desire! I do not want to be ashamed, fearful or timid concerning the Good News of Your salvation. I am so amazed by your love; I want to live by faith. "

A - *Adoration* _____

C - *Confession* _____

T - *Thanksgiving* _____

S - *Supplication* _____

Title: _____
Key Verse: _____
: _____

Chapter: _____

Greek Words: _____

SUFFER HARDSHIP LIKE...

RULES

IF

THEN

=

=

=

=

JOHN BUNYAN: TRUTH THROUGH

A dear Bunyan, not Paul
Is our hero today
No big blue ox for him,
And no lumberjack play.

This fine Bunyan, one John
Lived in England, you see
He was born long ago—
Seventeenth-century.

His dad wasn't rich, but
A good living he made
This tinker, pot-fixer
Taught his son the same trade.

But before long, John learned
Of the death-grip of sin
Then he opened his heart
And asked Christ to come in.

Saved, sealed, and forgiven,
Precious child of the King,
John soon traveled to preach
And the good news to bring.

But the state-sponsored church
Didn't like what he said
An arrest made his home
A bare jail cell instead.

For twelve years they kept him
But, true to God's call
John never stopped preaching
Not once, not at all.

Instead of his voice
Bunyan now used his pen
To write such a story
As we've not seen again.

Pilgrim's Progress, he called it
It's the one we know best
A tale of one Christian
And his journey toward rest.
Our man followed the call
Of Evangelist, who
Offered freedom and hope
And deliverance, too.

Christian listened to truth
And rejected the lies
Pressed on to the promise:
A home in the skies.

Our Bunyan's small story
Soon received world-wide fame.
And many who read it
Called the Savior by name.

The source of John's writing
Was his love for God's Word
As truth turned to story
Christ's message was heard.

When you think of Bunyan
Please remember our friend
And his tale, Pilgrim's Progress,
Of a life without end.

DAY ONE

ON MY KNEES:

We are starting a new chapter of 2 Timothy today! What a privilege it is to join you as we continue to mature in our understanding of the Word of God. Continue faithfully in the hard work of deeply investigating the Scriptures! Let's start again with prayer.

Pray. "Lord, I want to live in a way that shows I have the promise of You in my life. Show me Your grace and peace today as I seek You through the words of 2 Timothy."

Write. Advance! Turn to 2 Timothy 3:1-2 in your Bible and read the verses. Next, turn to a new page in the *"Write!"* section of your Sword Study. Purposefully write these first verses of Chapter 3 on the new page.

Read. Open your Bible to 2 Timothy 3 and read the chapter.

INVESTIGATIVE STUDY
STREETVIEW: CHAPTER 3

Apply!

Chapter 3 of 2 Timothy is an entire chapter describing the contrasts of two types of people. Go to the back of today's lesson and choose the "Chapter 3 Marking Sheet" in the version of your choice.

Mark each of the following words on your version of the "Chapter 3 Marking Sheet" using the symbols that we have provided you.

⛨ Jesus (or any names or pronouns referring to Him)

△ God, the Father

Circle and Place a Capital "P" above Paul

Circle and Place a Capital "T" above Timothy

☹ Men of Self

☺ Men of God

Underline with a squiggly line any form of the word persecute

📖 Any reference to God's Word

Noting all of the attributes of the two types of men in 2 Timothy allows us to visually see that Paul is focusing on the Men of Self. He is pointing out their characteristics so that we will know how to spot them. Do you think it also serves as a warning for us to make sure those characteristics don't describe our lives in any way?

Take a moment as we wrap up our INVESTIGATIVE STUDY portion today and find 2 Peter 3:3-9*. Read this Scripture and answer the short questions that follow below.

According to 2 Peter 3:3-10, what will be a sign of the last days?

_____

_____

What things did the Word of God reveal to men that they were ignoring?

_____

_____

_____

Why is the Lord slow to return to the earth? _____

_____

APPLY!

Using two to three of the descriptions for the Men of Self ☹, note an opposite characteristic. Ponder the contrasting attributes. Think about the people that surround you. How would an outsider peering into your daily lives characterize your group of friends and family? Do you look different from the rest of the world? Allow the Lord to confirm or convict your actions and use the result as a subject of your time in prayer.

A.C.T.S. PRAYER TIME

Going forward, we would like you to fill in your own "mini" prayer journal in the A.C.T.S. letters below. Try to personalize your prayers with what God has spoken to you during your study. Occasionally, you will be encouraged to look back over your prayer notes to see how God has answered your supplications and matured your faith.

A - Adoration_____

C - Confession_____

T - Thanksgiving_____

S - Supplication_____

DIGGING DEEPER

Summarize why 2 Peter 3:3-9 relates to what you have been learning. Create 2 or 3 investigative questions for the passage in the space below. Finally, memorize it!

King James Version - 2 Timothy, Chapter 3 - Marking Sheet

[1]This know also, that in the last days perilous times shall come. [2]For men shall be lovers of their own selves, covetous, boasters, proud, blasphemers, disobedient to parents, unthankful, unholy, [3]Without natural affection, trucebreakers, false accusers, incontinent, fierce, despisers of those that are good, [4]Traitors, heady, highminded, lovers of pleasures more than lovers of God; [5]Having a form of godliness, but denying the power thereof: from such turn away. [6]For of this sort are they which creep into houses, and lead captive silly women laden with sins, led away with divers lusts, [7]Ever learning, and never able to come to the knowledge of the truth. [8]Now as Jannes and Jambres withstood Moses, so do these also resist the truth: men of corrupt minds, reprobate concerning the faith. [9]But they shall proceed no further: for their folly shall be manifest unto all men, as their's also was. [10]But thou hast fully known my doctrine, manner of life, purpose, faith, longsuffering, charity, patience, [11]Persecutions, afflictions, which came unto me at Antioch, at Iconium, at Lystra; what persecutions I endured: but out of them all the Lord delivered me. [12]Yea, and all that will live godly in Christ Jesus shall suffer persecution. [13]But evil men and seducers shall wax worse and worse, deceiving, and being deceived. [14]But continue thou in the things which thou hast learned and hast been assured of, knowing of whom thou hast learned them; [15]And that from a child thou hast known the holy scriptures, which are able to make thee wise unto salvation through faith which is in Christ Jesus. [16]All scripture is given by inspiration of God, and is profitable for doctrine, for reproof, for correction, for instruction in righteousness: [17]That the man of God may be perfect, thoroughly furnished unto all good works.

New International Version – 2 Timothy, Chapter 3 – Marking Sheet

¹ But mark this: There will be terrible times in the last days. ² People will be lovers of themselves, lovers of money, boastful, proud, abusive, disobedient to their parents, ungrateful, unholy, ³ without love, unforgiving, slanderous, without self-control, brutal, not lovers of the good, ⁴ treacherous, rash, conceited, lovers of pleasure rather than lovers of God— ⁵ having a form of godliness but denying its power. Have nothing to do with them. ⁶ They are the kind who worm their way into homes and gain control over weak-willed women, who are loaded down with sins and are swayed by all kinds of evil desires, ⁷ always learning but never able to acknowledge the truth. ⁸ Just as Jannes and Jambres opposed Moses, so also these men oppose the truth—men of depraved minds, who, as far as the faith is concerned, are rejected. ⁹ But they will not get very far because, as in the case of those men, their folly will be clear to everyone. ¹⁰ You, however, know all about my teaching, my way of life, my purpose, faith, patience, love, endurance, ¹¹ persecutions, sufferings—what kinds of things happened to me in Antioch, Iconium and Lystra, the persecutions I endured. Yet the Lord rescued me from all of them. ¹² In fact, everyone who wants to live a godly life in Christ Jesus will be persecuted, ¹³ while evil men and impostors will go from bad to worse, deceiving and being deceived. ¹⁴ But as for you, continue in what you have learned and have become convinced of, because you know those from whom you learned it, ¹⁵ and how from infancy you have known the holy Scriptures, which are able to make you wise for salvation through faith in Christ Jesus. ¹⁶ All Scripture is God-breathed and is useful for teaching, rebuking, correcting and training in righteousness, ¹⁷ so that the man of God may be thoroughly equipped for every good work.

New King James Version – 2 Timothy, Chapter 3 – Marking Sheet

[1] But know this, that in the last days perilous times will come: [2] For men will be lovers of themselves, lovers of money, boasters, proud, blasphemers, disobedient to parents, unthankful, unholy, [3] unloving, unforgiving, slanderers, without self-control, brutal, despisers of good, [4] traitors, headstrong, haughty, lovers of pleasure rather than lovers of God, [5] having a form of godliness but denying its power. And from such people turn away! [6] For of this sort are those who creep into households and make captives of gullible women loaded down with sins, led away by various lusts, [7] always learning and never able to come to the knowledge of the truth. [8] Now as Jannes and Jambres resisted Moses, so do these also resist the truth: men of corrupt minds, disapproved concerning the faith; [9] but they will progress no further, for their folly will be manifest to all, as theirs also was. [10] But you have carefully followed my doctrine, manner of life, purpose, faith, longsuffering, love, perseverance, [11] persecutions, afflictions, which happened to me at Antioch, at Iconium, at Lystra—what persecutions I endured. And out of them all the Lord delivered me. [12] Yes, and all who desire to live godly in Christ Jesus will suffer persecution. [13] But evil men and impostors will grow worse and worse, deceiving and being deceived. [14] But you must continue in the things which you have learned and been assured of, knowing from whom you have learned them, [15] and that from childhood you have known the Holy Scriptures, which are able to make you wise for salvation through faith which is in Christ Jesus. [16] All Scripture is given by inspiration of God, and is profitable for doctrine, for reproof, for correction, for instruction in righteousness, [17] that the man of God may be complete, thoroughly equipped for every good work.

New American Standard Bible – 2 Timothy, Chapter 3 – Marking Sheet

[1] But realize this, that in the last days difficult times will come. [2] For men will be lovers of self, lovers of money, boastful, arrogant, revilers, disobedient to parents, ungrateful, unholy, [3] unloving, irreconcilable, malicious gossips, without self-control, brutal, haters of good, [4] treacherous, reckless, conceited, lovers of pleasure rather than lovers of God, [5] holding to a form of godliness, although they have denied its power; Avoid such men as these. [6] For among them are those who enter into households and captivate weak women weighed down with sins, led on by various impulses, [7] always learning and never able to come to the knowledge of the truth. [8] Just as Jannes and Jambres opposed Moses, so these men also oppose the truth, men of depraved mind, rejected in regard to the faith. [9] But they will not make further progress; for their folly will be obvious to all, just as Jannes's and Jambres's folly was also. [10] Now you followed my teaching, conduct, purpose, faith, patience, love, perseverance, [11] persecutions, and sufferings, such as happened to me at Antioch, at Iconium and at Lystra; what persecutions I endured, and out of them all the Lord rescued me! [12] Indeed, all who desire to live godly in Christ Jesus will be persecuted. [13] But evil men and impostors will proceed from bad to worse, deceiving and being deceived. [14] You, however, continue in the things you have learned and become convinced of, knowing from whom you have learned them, [15] and that from childhood you have known the sacred writings which are able to give you the wisdom that leads to salvation through faith which is in Christ Jesus. [16] All Scripture is inspired by God and profitable for teaching, for reproof, for correction, for training in righteousness; [17] so that the man of God may be adequate, equipped for every good work.

English Standard Version – 2 Timothy, Chapter 3 – Marking Sheet

[1] But understand this, that in the last days there will come times of difficulty. [2] For people will be lovers of self, lovers of money, proud, arrogant, abusive, disobedient to their parents, ungrateful, unholy, [3] heartless, unappeasable, slanderous, without self-control, brutal, not loving good, [4] treacherous, reckless, swollen with conceit, lovers of pleasure rather than lovers of God, [5] having the appearance of godliness, but denying its power. Avoid such people. [6] For among them are those who creep into households and capture weak women, burdened with sins and led astray by various passions, [7] always learning and never able to arrive at a knowledge of the truth. [8] Just as Jannes and Jambres opposed Moses, so these men also oppose the truth, men corrupted in mind and disqualified regarding the faith. [9] But they will not get very far, for their folly will be plain to all, as was that of those two men. [10] You, however, have followed my teaching, my conduct, my aim in life, my faith, my patience, my love, my steadfastness, [11] my persecutions and sufferings that happened to me at Antioch, at Iconium, and at Lystra—which persecutions I endured; yet from them all the Lord rescued me. [12] Indeed, all who desire to live a godly life in Christ Jesus will be persecuted, [13] while evil people and impostors will go on from bad to worse, deceiving and being deceived. [14] But as for you, continue in what you have learned and have firmly believed, knowing from whom you learned it [15] and how from childhood you have been acquainted with the sacred writings, which are able to make you wise for salvation through faith in Christ Jesus. [16] All Scripture is breathed out by God and profitable for teaching, for reproof, for correction, and for training in righteousness, [17] that the man of God may be complete, equipped for every good work.

DAY TWO

ON MY KNEES:

A new sunrise and a fresh day are here for us to dive into the Word and fellowship with the Lord. If you get nothing else accomplished in your day but meeting with the Lord, you have accomplished much. For many a person, believers included, days go by without any thought or time with the Lord. Remain faithful! Come, and let us pray.

Pray. "Jesus, You have power over death and sin. I praise You for freeing me from the penalty, presence and power of sin. Keep this in the forefront of mind today as I make each choice. As I write Your words, please etch them on my heart.

Write. Please write 2 Timothy 3:3-5. As you do that, consider what you are writing. Does it seem as though our current culture sounds like the days described in these verses?

Read. Decisively read the first three chapters of 2 Timothy through Chapter 3 to hear the flow of the letter as you add the new chapter.

INVESTIGATIVE STUDY
STREETVIEW: CHAPTER 3

Apply!

Today, we are going to interview 2 Timothy, Chapter 3 by asking various "who, what, why, where and how" questions of the text. Be sure to answer the questions using only what you find in Scripture. Let's begin right away.

Who are the characters of Chapter 3?

_____ _____

_____ _____

_____ _____

How can we tell when we are nearing the last days, according to verses 1 and 2?

_____

Who do the men in verses 2-4 love?

_____

Summarize how the Men of God are characterized, according to verses 10-11 and 14-15?

_____

_____

What new locations does verse 11 mention?

_____

What is a "given" for the Christian, according to verse 12?

_____

According to verse 13, while Men of God are continuing to be persecuted, what are three things that the Men of Self are doing?

_____   _____   _____

List the contrast between how the Men of Self and the Men of God handle the Scriptures.

Men of Self ….

_____ (Verse 7)

_____ (Verse 9)

Men of God…

_____ (Verse 14)

APPLY!

The Greek word used for "lovers" of self has a root of ***phileo***, which is a type of love that closely relates to friendship. In a surprising twist, Paul used a word that basically says they are all about being friends with themselves (and money). A person carefully nurtures and cares for a friend, don't they? These Men of Self were taking care of their best friend – themselves!

Note some ways that you can keep yourself from focusing on yourself and focus on Christ instead.

_____

_____

A.C.T.S. PRAYER TIME

A - *Adoration* _____

C - *Confession* _____

T - *Thanksgiving* _____

S - *Supplication* _____

DIGGING DEEPER

Investigate Paul's missionary travels, Timothy's travels and their travels together.

DAY THREE

Do you realize that what you are about to do is uncommon? Around the world, so few pause to recognize the Ruler of rulers, King of kings and Creator of all things. May you stay the course, run the race and continue to draw near to Him today through the study of His great book.

Pray. "Lord, I want to serve you with a clear conscience. I want to understand what that means in my life. Teach me Your ways today so that I might follow them for the rest of my days."

Write. Once you are set, turn and read 2 Timothy 3:6-7. Allow the words to soak in as you write them in your copy of 2 Timothy.

Read. Open your Bible to 2 Timothy 3 and read the chapter before beginning your study.

INVESTIGATIVE STUDY
STREETVIEW: CHAPTER 3

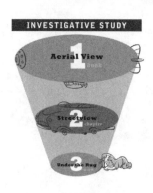

Apply!

Paul begins Chapter 3 using the Greek word "ginosko" which means to know, understand, be aware of or realize. The modern way we might express this could be, "Pay attention... I want you to get this!" He goes on to describe that difficult times are coming because people are going to be characterized as Men of Self instead of Men of God. He continues to emphasize that followers of Christ will be persecuted and need to be equipped by the Word of God for good works.

Regardless of how close we are to being smack dab in the middle of the time Paul was referring to, we are much closer than Paul was when he wrote these words 2,000 years ago. His message is extremely pertinent to us now! He is going to contrast the person who loves himself with the person who loves God by rattling off lists of their characteristics. To see clearly the two "men" that Paul describes, we will complete two charts. Do not be overwhelmed by all the blanks in the charts – we will take it one-step at a time over the next few days. You will be amazed at all that you learn through Paul's descriptive lists! We will begin with the "Men of Self" chart.

Fill in the characteristics (in verses 2-5) of the Men of Self. Next, look up the definitions for the first half of the characteristics that you found. Tomorrow, we will complete the remaining definitions.

	Men of Self	Definition	Reference	Insights
1				
2				
3				
4				
5				
6				
7				
8				
9				
10				
11				
12				
13				
14				
15				
16				
17				
18				
19				
20				
21				
22				

*Note: the number of adjectives and descriptions are different in each version so you might not use all the blanks above.

Additional descriptions of the Men of Self are found hidden within verses 6 through 13. What additional notes would you add concerning these people?

_____

_____

APPLY!

Pull up a news app or website, or grab a daily newspaper or magazine, such as God's World Magazine. Look at the Table of Contents, skim through the headlines and choose a couple of the major stories. Note a few examples of any of the characteristics of man that Paul warned Timothy about in 2 Timothy on the lines below.

_____

_____

_____

A.C.T.S. PRAYER TIME

A - *Adoration*_____

C - *Confession*_____

T - *Thanksgiving*_____

S - *Supplication*_____

DIGGING DEEPER

Do you enjoy reading?

"The Genesis Flood" by John C Whitcomb and Henry M. Morris is an excellent resource to understand the Biblical perspective of the Flood.

Have you read Pilgrim's Progress? If not, please do. If so, which lesson Christian learned on his journey has the most significance for your life?

D A Y   F O U R

ON MY KNEES:

How blessed is the man who finds wisdom, for nothing is more valuable or compares to the wisdom of God. Focus on your study, and don't let the prize depart from your sight for the rewards of the knowledge of God's ways are without boundaries! Go before your Lord in prayer.

Pray. " 'Abba, Father': I have read it, heard it proclaimed and listened to it in songs, but I want to truly feel like You are my "Daddy." I can be so dependent on only what I can see, so please help me to have more faith. Use Your words to soften the hardened soil of my heart. In Jesus' name, Amen."

Write. Neatly write 2 Timothy 3:8-9 in the *"Write!"* section of your Sword Study.

Read. Today, read 2 Timothy 3 out loud for a change of pace.

INVESTIGATIVE STUDY

Apply!

Begin by finishing your remaining definitions on your "Men of Self" Chart.

Now, we will show you a passage of Scripture to further define some of the attributes. We have done this by simply looking in a Bible concordance for the word or topic. We selected a few to add Biblical insight to Paul's descriptive words. You can do this on your own, too! After you do ours, do the remaining ones on your own. Be aware, there may be a few that aren't found anywhere else in the Bible.

Look up the following passages. After you have read them, transfer the reference to the column marked "reference" on your "Men of Self" chart and put any notes to yourself that you learned in the "Insights" column. Remember, we haven't done all of them, but you are welcome to add others to your chart.

James 3:16-18
Colossians 3:22
Proverbs 6:16-19
1 Timothy 1:9

APPLY!

Do not be discouraged if it feels like the Men of Self outnumber the Men of God. Turn to Psalm 9:1-4* in your Bible. Take a few minutes to write down all the Lord has done for you. When you close in prayer, remember to thank the Lord for all He has done!

_____

_____

_____

_____

A.C.T.S. PRAYER TIME

A - Adoration_____

C - Confession_____

T - Thanksgiving_____

S - Supplication_____

D A Y   F I V E

ON MY KNEES:

We gain God's insight through the diligent study of His Word. He will use you in mighty ways as you grow through your studying. Continue in your diligence, my friend, continue on! Let's pray first.

Pray. "Lord, thank you for saving me. You are a great and gracious God, full of mercy and lovingkindness. I continue to be amazed and humbled by Your love. Keep me awestruck and focused on Your Word as my Daily Bread. In Jesus' name, Amen. "

Write. Turn back to your writing pages and copy 2 Timothy 3:10-11 on your next available line.

Read. Once again, please turn to Chapter 3 of 2 Timothy and read through the chapter.

INVESTIGATIVE STUDY
STREETVIEW: CHAPTER 3

INVESTIGATIVE STUDY

Apply!

Today, we will turn our attention to the "Men of God" who stand out in sharp contrast to the "Men of Self." In Chapter 3, Paul gives us a list of characteristics that describe godly people. Just as we did with the "Men of Self," we will fill in the characteristics column and then insert short definitions for each attribute. Remember, depending on your Bible version, you may not fill in all the blanks.

	Men of God	Definition	Reference	Insights
1				
2				
3				
4				
5				
6				
7				
8				
9				
10				
11				
12				
13				

As we close, we will give you a few other Scriptures that further define the godly men's characteristics. After you complete the ones that we give you, plan on doing the remaining on your own. Concluding our week with the encouragement and exhortations for a godly person is such a positive way to end our week! Ask God to apply these truths to your own life, and enjoy seeing the blessings of walking with the Lord in an upright manner!

Deuteronomy 7:9

Proverbs 28:20

Titus 2:12

Acts 17:11

1 Thessalonians 3:3-4

Before you stop for the day, begin to look over Chapter 3 and think about the verse that you would chose as the key verse of the chapter. What title would you chose for this chapter? You could even turn back to Week 1, Day 5 and see what title you came up with then. Would you choose differently now? Write a short note to yourself about any thoughts on the key verse and changes in your title in the lines below:

_____

_____

APPLY!

Next week, we will study the word Scripture. Spend some time on the internet or at the library to look at quotes about the Bible. If you are able, this link is a great example of listings: http://www.internationalwallofprayer.org/Q-01-FAMOUS-QUOTES.html

A.C.T.S. PRAYER TIME

A - Adoration_____

C - Confession_____

T - Thanksgiving_____

S - Supplication_____

TRUE LIES:
WILLIAM TYNDALE

My dear friends,

My time in prison wears on me, but the rumors have been flying, so I thought it best I take time to address a few. Better the truth from my pen than lies from those who misunderstand my intentions.

RUMOR:

Only an old man would be capable of the massive work required to translate the Bible into English.

TRUTH:

I was born in 1494. I enrolled in Oxford at the tender age of eleven and earned my Master's degree at twenty-one. At this writing, I'm more than forty years of age—growing older, to be sure, but not yet old.

RUMOR:

Someone else did my translating for me because I only know English.

TRUTH:

I'm fluent in eight languages: Hebrew, Greek, Latin, Spanish, French, Italian, German, and of course English. I recognize my language abilities as a gift from God.

RUMOR:

My goal in translating the Bible is to become rich and famous.

TRUTH:

My goal is to put the Holy Scriptures into the language of the people (English) for the first time. My heart burns to share the good news of Christ and the doctrine of justification

(Christ's death, not our works, gives us right standing with God) through my work. I added special notes to my translation to make my viewpoint clear.

RUMOR:

I am a tool in the hands of those in power.

TRUTH:

My thinking seems to anger everyone. The Catholic Church disagrees with my doctrine, and so does King Henry VIII.

RUMOR:

I deserted my homeland and countrymen when I completed the translation overseas.

TRUTH:

I left England for Europe after it became apparent my work had no support at home. In 1525, in Worms ("vœrms"), Germany, God granted a miracle: my first New Testament, a direct translation from Greek to English.

RUMOR:

Church and government leaders loved this first translation so much they bought up all the copies.

TRUTH:

We smuggled the first translation into England and the authorities hated it. They bought up all the copies they could in order to prevent its spread. They did all they could to silence me.

RUMOR:

I used other translations, not the original languages, to produce my Bible.

TRUTH:

I worked from manuscripts as close to the original as I could. After my first Bible appeared, I moved to Antwerp, Belgium, where I worked for nine years. During this time, I finished a fresh translation of the New Testament and began work on the Old.

RUMOR:

My translation of the Bible is the only real work I've done.

TRUTH:

I have worked as a preacher, evangelist, and author of several tracts and other spiritual writings.

RUMOR:

I spend day and night working on my translation and rarely see people.

TRUTH:

In prison or out, I make it a point to give myself to good works that show my love for Christ. I make friends with the poor and hurting. I also do my best to read Scripture before and after every meal no matter who is dining with me.

RUMOR:

I was arrested for my lack of care in translating the Scriptures.

TRUTH:

I was arrested for heresy (teaching false beliefs) after a former friend betrayed me.

RUMOR:

I am angry at God over the imprisonment.

TRUTH:

I trust God to work out my time in prison for my good and His glory.

RUMOR:

I take advantage of the state while awaiting trial and live in a luxurious castle.

TRUTH:

I have been imprisoned in the castle Vilvoorden for close to 500 days. I wish not to complain, but conditions are far from luxurious. I have, however, used the time to continue my translation work whenever I can.

Thank you for your kind attention to the truth. Whatever happens to me, I trust you will base your opinion of God not on my circumstances but on the truths of His Word. If He is on our side, it does not matter who is against us.

I trust you will join me in standing for truth—now and forevermore.

Yours in faith,

William Tyndale

Officials from the Holy Roman Empire condemned William Tyndale as a heretic and sentenced him to death. On October 6, 1536, they offered him a chance to recant (turn his back on his faith). He refused and was given a moment to pray before being hanged, then burned at the stake. His prayer, "Lord, open the King of England's eyes," was answered three years after his death when King Henry VIII published the Scriptures in English as "The Great Bible."

Tyndale was the first person to print an English version New Testament. Only one copy still exists, for which the British Museum paid two million dollars in 1948. One year after his death, Tyndale's friend John Rogers produced the Matthew-Tyndale Bible, the first printing of a complete English language Bible translated directly from the original Greek and Hebrew.

D A Y   O N E

ON MY KNEES:

Wisdom continues to call you to the pages of God's Word. How will you answer today? Receive instruction from His precepts and you will grow in wisdom and knowledge, and your love for your heavenly Father will increase as you come to know Him more! Make time to come before Him in humble adoration as you pray today.

Pray. " Father, thank You for the gift of faithful friends. I am so appreciative of those that You have given me to support, encourage and love me in the faith. They are indeed a great refreshment to my soul. Help me to be a faithful friend to many for your sake."

Write. 2 Timothy 3:12-13.

Read. 2 Timothy, Chapter 3

INVESTIGATIVE STUDY
UNDER THE RUG: KEY WORDS AND WORD STUDIES

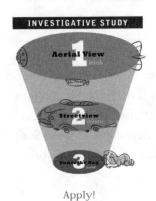

Apply!

Normally, at this stage in our INVESTIGATIVE STUDY, we mark all of the key words of the chapter. We are going to do something a little different now, however. You have read Chapter 3 a number of times. Write a short, three to four sentence summary of the chapter in the lines below.

_____

_____

_____

_____

_____

Now, which verse(s) would you chose as the key passage? _____

We have decided to use 2 Timothy 3:16-17*, which is also one of our Focus Scriptures for our Sword Study. Please read these two verses and then use them to answer the detailed questions below.

How much of Scripture is inspired? _____

Who inspired Scripture? _____

Why is Scripture profitable or useful in our lives?

_____ _____ _____

_____ _____ _____

Who does the man described belong to, according to verse 17?

_____

_____

What impact does Scripture have on the man?

_____

_____

What is the man prepared to do?

_____

_____

To sum up, Paul says that in the last days difficult times will come. We can recognize those days because men will love themselves and even though they may act as if they uphold godliness, they are not depending on God's power. On the other hand, lovers of God are following Paul's teachings and way of living. They are equipped to work for God through their dependence on the Scriptures. Quickly read the word study of *Scripture* below before closing your time in the Scriptures!

Word Study:

PART A: If you were to look up the word *Scripture* in Strong's Concordance, you would find that the Strong's number assigned to it is 1124. We will use this number to look up the detailed explanation of the Greek word in Part B. Below are the transliteration, the pronunciation, and the basic definition from the Strong's lexicon.

1124. *graphe. graf-ay*; from 1125; a document, i.e. holy Writ – writing. To describe. Used in plural to mean the entire or singular to mean a part of it.

PART B: If you look up these numbers in another Greek lexicon, you can discover further explanation of the meanings in Greek as seen here:

1) Used in the plural in the New Testament for the Holy Scriptures, or in the singular for part of it.

"The Holy Scriptures are everywhere termed as the, 'the', graphe, 'Scripture', giving it authoritativeness."

PART C: During our investigation of the word *Scripture*, we found that the word *graphe* is almost invariably preceded by an article (i.e. meaning all or part) and will have added descriptions to emphasize that they are the set apart writings of the Holy God, such as God-breathed, inspired and holy.

"The Scriptures being holy refers to their established authority whose purpose produces holiness, separation from sin and unto God. No sinner can long read the Scriptures without a change taking place in his or her life. Either he or she will change in a supernatural way or the Scriptures will not be read for long. The Scriptures are an authoritative document of God which produces holiness.

The word grammata, writings, in 2 Timothy 3:15, 'And that from a child thou hast known the Holy Scriptures,' is ta hiera grammata, the sacred writings which were sacred for religious training versus mundane learning. Timothy is reminded by Paul of his training (emathes, 'thou has learned' in 2 Timothy 3:14, indicating not only being taught but actually learning). In 2 Timothy 3:16 Paul uses pasa (3956), all, meaning every part of the whole and all of it together, and graphe, Scripture, and not grammata as he used in verse fifteen. It is as if Paul were to say to Timothy, "From your babyhood up you were exposed to and learned the available religions and sacred (hiera) writing, but now we have the Scriptures (the graphe), that which has been written once and for all and constitutes the final authority of God's revelation. We thus conclude that grammata should never be taken as Holy Scripture."

We would be remise if we didn't take a moment to note how important studying the Word of God is to our lives. We need to hear directly from the mouth of God. We do not need "how-to" books, relational fiction stories or motivational talks, ultimately. We need be in the Word of God ourselves, sitting under the Teacher of teachers, the Holy Spirit. And...we need to bring others along to do the same. God's Word will save His people. Conclude by reading Romans 15:4 and writing it on the lines below:

_____

_____

_____

APPLY!

How many facts do you know by heart about the Bible? List all that you know about the Scriptures on the lines below.

_____

_____

_____

_____

A.C.T.S. PRAYER TIME

A - *Adoration*_____

C - *Confession*_____

T - *Thanksgiving*_____

S - *Supplication*_____

"The BIBLE — banned, burned, beloved. More widely read, more frequently attacked than any other book in history. Generations of intellectuals have attempted to discredit it; dictators of every age have outlawed it and executed those who read it. Yet soldiers carry it into battle believing it more powerful than their weapons. Fragments of it smuggled into solitary prison cells have transformed ruthless killers into gentle saints."
~Charles Colson~

D A Y   T W O

ON MY KNEES:

We can hardly wait for you to get to your study. It is at these times we feel like rushing right into the Word. Yet, it is at these very times, it is so important to stop and pray.

Pray. "Jesus, help me hear Your words, not my thoughts, about what I read today. Please miraculously silence all the noise around me. I want to hear Your words speak directly to my heart."

Write. 2 Timothy 3:14

Read. Whoa…slow down! Read just verses 14-17 of 2 Timothy before you begin your INVESTIGATIVE STUDY.

Apply!

INVESTIGATIVE STUDY
SCRIPTURE CROSS REFERENCES

One of the very important aspects of studying the Word through your Sword Study is that we want you to hear Scripture support Scripture. Therefore, you are going to look at the various verses in 2 Timothy that Paul emphasizes the *Scriptures* (or words based on *Scripture*) and then other passages that describe the importance of God's Word. Soak in the importance of these truths, for the Word is how the man of God is equipped for all things in life. Note: We will not review 2 Timothy 2:16-17 since we focused on it at the end of last week.

Scripture mentioned in 2 Timothy

2 Timothy 1:13

What phrase in 2 Timothy 1:13 refers to *Scripture* in some way?

_____

_____

By whom were these words spoken?

_____

_____

In whom are these words grounded?

_____

_____

How are these words to be handled?

_____

_____

2 Timothy 2:8-9

What phrase in this passage refers to *Scripture*?

_____

What cannot hinder the effectiveness of *Scripture*?

_____

What is a part of *Scripture*, according to this passage (vs 8)?

_____

2 Timothy 2:15

What phrase in this passage refers to *Scripture*?

_____

What is the key word used to described the word?

_____

What is the definition of truth?

_____

2 Timothy 4:2

What is *Scripture* called in this passage?

_____

What is to be done with it?

_____

When is this to be done?

_____

We know you are running out of time and we do not want you to rush by the many passages that highlight the importance of *Scripture*, so we will have to continue with cross references tomorrow. We pray that you have a feeling of great anticipation for the treasures you will see when you return!

APPLY!

What would make the Scriptures more accessible to you? What would make you call on them more frequently to answer a day's problem or situation?

"Siri, your wish is its command… Siri on iPhone 4S lets you use your voice to send messages, schedule meetings, place phone calls, and more. Ask Siri to do things just by talking the way you talk. Siri understands what you say, knows what you mean, and even talks back. Siri is so easy to use and does so much, you'll keep finding more and more ways to use it"

The new iPhones have a great new feature available to its users called "Siri".
Ask Siri any question and she will go search the internet for an answer to your question.

"Hi Siri, where is the nearest McDonalds?"

"Hello ma'am, the nearest McDonalds is 2 miles from your location,
would you like me to map it for you?"

"Hello Siri, who created the world?"

"Hello ma'am, just a minute I am still searching the web for a truthful answer to that question."

Eventually, the world might look to Siri for truth, but as Believers, we know that *the* truth can only be found in the Word of God.

Think of some practical ways to get the Word of God in front of yourself. Download a Bible app on your phone, load a new Bible Software program on your PC, stick "Scripture Stickies" on all of your mirrors or put Scripture on your walls, use an online tool like ScriptureTyper.com. While you are at it, memorize another verse so it is *graphe* on your heart!

A.C.T.S. PRAYER TIME

A - *Adoration* _____

C - *Confession* _____

T - *Thanksgiving* _____

S - *Supplication* _____

DIGGING DEEPER

There are roughly 6,500 spoken languages in the world today. However, about 2,000 of those languages have fewer than 1,000 speakers. Mandarin Chinese tops the list of most popular world languages, with over a billion speakers. English trails in third place, with just over 320 million speakers. This data includes all speakers of the languages, not only native speakers.

Take some time to investigate the translation process by visiting The Seed Company's website at www.TheSeedCompany.org

Language	Approx. number of speakers
1. Chinese (Mandarin)	1,213,000,000
2. Spanish	329,000,000
3. English	328,000,000
4. Arabic	221,000,000
5. Hindi1	182,000,000
6. Bengali	181,000,000
7. Portuguese	178,000,000
8. Russian	144,000,000
9. Japanese	122,000,000
10. German	90,000,000

Source: Ethnologue, 16th Edition.

DAY THREE

ON MY KNEES:

In Proverbs, Wisdom cries, "I love those who love me" and promises that "those who diligently seek" her will find her. This is *you*, my friend in the Lord. Even when it is difficult and you come half-heartedly to meet with Him in prayer and study, He comes eagerly to meet with you. He is faithful. Share your heart with Him and He will answer.

Pray. "Lord, I hear Your call to train myself during these days that I might be effective at proclaiming Your salvation to others regardless of the cost. Prepare me for the hardships ahead and help me to think above the things of everyday life. Holy Spirit, be my Teacher today."

Write. Enthusiastically write 2 Timothy 3:15. Truly, write this verse with a different flair to your writing style so that you might highlight it in a different way than the other verses you have written because it is packed with special meaning. Your future study will surely show this to be true.

Read. Turn to Chapter 3 of 2 Timothy before you begin studying.

INVESTIGATIVE STUDY
SCRIPTURE CROSS REFERENCES

Prepare to turn to passages throughout your Bible as we seek to confirm the importance of God's Word in our lives for teaching, reproof, correction, instruction in righteousness so that as children of God we may perfected and prepared for all good works! Look up each of the following passages and note what you learn about the Scriptures on the line provided.

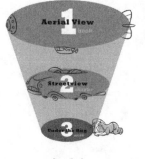

Apply!

Psalm 119:9: _____

John 5:39-40: _____

John 17:17: _____

Isaiah 40:7-8: _____

Isaiah 55:11: _____

Proverbs 2:6: _____

Hebrews 4:12: _____

_____

1 Peter 1:23: _____

APPLY!

Are you aware there is a chapter in the Bible that uses a word or phrase in nearly every verse that refers to the *Scriptures*? Psalm 119 is an entire chapter set aside proclaiming the Word over and over. Turn to it and write as many different words/phrases representing *Scripture* as you are able.

_____ _____ _____
_____ _____ _____
_____ _____ _____
_____ _____ _____
_____ _____ _____

A . C . T . S .   P R A Y E R   T I M E

A - *Adoration*_____

C - *Confession*_____

T - *Thanksgiving*_____

S - *Supplication*_____

DAY FOUR

ON MY KNEES:

Are you feeling encouraged by the Lord as you approach His Word today? Many are praying for you as you continue to persevere in the diligence of studying God's Word daily. Begin your time alone with the Lord in prayer.

Pray. "Father, give me understanding as I approach Your words in 2 Timothy so that I may learn more about You and Your commandments. I want to be known as a child of God and an example to others as they see me live out what Your Word says. I want to glorify You." Remind my heart that these are not man's words, but words from You, as my Creator."

Write 2 Timothy 3:16-17*

Read. Please read 2 Timothy, Chapter 3 once again.

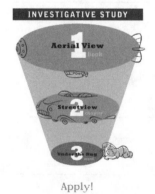

Apply!

INVESTIGATIVE STUDY
SCRIPTURE WORD STUDY:

PERSECUTE(D)

PART A: If you were to look up the words *persecute/persecutions* in Strong's Concordance, you would find that the Strong's numbers assigned to them are 1375 and 1377. We will use these numbers to look up the detailed explanation of the Greek words in Part B. Below are the transliterations (the way the word is written in English), the pronunciation, and the basic definition from the Strong's lexicon (dictionary).

1375. *Diogmos*, *dee-ogue-mos*; from 1377, persecution.

1377. *Dioko*, *dee-o-ko*, to persecute, ensue, follow after, given to suffer, press toward.

PART B: If you look up these numbers in another Greek lexicon, you can discover further explanation of their meanings in Greek as seen here:

1) To pursue, prosecute with repeated acts of enmity

   a.) Enmity: hate, hostility, antagonism, opposition, aggression

2) To purse with eagerness and diligence to obtain

PART C: Turn to 2 Timothy 3:11-12 to see how these definitions help you better understand how Paul used the words *persecute* and *persecutions* in his letter to us.

Paul uses the words *persecuted* and *persecutions* to describe what he has gone through for the sake of the Scriptures and the gospel. He also reminds and warns Timothy that he will experience the same, and when he does, he should react in patience and recollection of all that he has been taught through the Scriptures and Paul's teachings. We can further understand all this entails through studying additional cross references to the words *persecute* and *persecutions*.

Refer to the following passages and summarize the additional insights you gain on the lines next to the references.

2 Corinthians 12:7:

_____

Galatians 1:11-17*:

_____

John 15:20:

_____

Matthew 13:20-21:

_____

Acts 14:19-20:

_____

Mark 10:29-31

_____

2 Thessalonians 1:3-5

_____

Acts 13:50:

_____

Romans 8:34-39

_____

APPLY!

Be still, and know that I am God . . . —Psalm 46:10

"Perseverance is more than endurance. It is endurance combined with absolute assurance and certainty that what we are looking for is going to happen. Perseverance means more than just hanging on, which may be only exposing our fear of letting go and falling. Perseverance is our supreme effort of refusing to believe that our hero is going to be conquered. Our greatest fear is that somehow Jesus Christ will be defeated. Also, our fear is that the very things our Lord stood for— love, justice, forgiveness, and kindness among men— will not win out in the end and will represent an unattainable goal for us. Then there is the call to spiritual perseverance. A call not to hang on and do nothing, but to work deliberately, knowing with certainty that God will never be defeated.

If our hopes seem to be experiencing disappointment right now, it simply means that they are being purified. Every hope or dream of the human mind will be fulfilled if it is noble and of God. But one of the greatest stresses in life is the stress of waiting for God. He brings fulfillment, 'because you have kept My command to persevere…' Revelation 3:10" [6]

Be honest with yourself. What do you think about Paul saying that you will face persecution? Write how you feel about that here: _____

_____

Look up Deuteronomy 31:6*. Why do you think God said the words in Deuteronomy?

_____

Share how you feel about this with the Lord during your closing prayer time.

A.C.T.S. PRAYER TIME

A - *Adoration*_____

C - *Confession*_____

T - *Thanksgiving*_____

S - *Supplication*_____

"I have one desire now - to live a life of reckless abandon for the Lord,
putting all my energy and strength into it."
~Elisabeth Elliot, Through Gates of Splendor: 40th Anniversary Edition~

DAY FIVE

ON MY KNEES:

Pray. "Lord, give me a calm and quiet spirit today as I conclude my study of 2 Timothy 3. Help me to summarize my thoughts so that I might be able to look back on them years from now and clearly remember all that you have taught me. There are many instructions and I need Your help to bring them to my mind as I live my life daily before lost people and the other "Timothy's" in my life. In Your powerful name, I pray. Amen. "

Write- Skim through your copy of 2 Timothy 3 marking any references to God.

Read. Today, read completely through 2 Timothy as you conclude your investigative study on Chapter 3.

Apply!

INVESTIGATIVE STUDY
1-2-3 CHAPTER 3 – SUMMARIZE!

Chapter 3 Summary:

We have arrived to another *"Day 10 Diagram"*.

Remember, if you have any problems figuring out how to fill in your *Day 10 Diagram*, talk to a parent; the Parent Guidebook includes the key to this diagram.

☐ To begin, look at the top of the Day 10 Diagram. Fill in the chapter number and the title that you created for this chapter.

☐ Next, which verse from the chapter do you think was the "key verse?"

☐ Beside the heart, list the references to any Bible passages that you have hidden in your heart during your study of Chapter 3.

☐ On the right of the page, transfer your key Greek words from this chapter and write a shortened definition of their meanings.

☐ On the bottom of the *Diagram* page, transfer the most important things that you learned about God through marking the references about Him in your Write! Tab. If you run out of space, continue on the back side of your Diagram.

Every young Timothy will encounter many types of people in the world as they follow Jesus, but as times grow more difficult towards the end of human history, Paul wants to warn every disciple to specifically note two types of people: the Men of Self and the Men of God.

On your Diagram, label the representatives shown as Men of Self or Men of God beneath their feet. If only all Timothy's would heed such warning and strive to follow Paul's example as he followed the example of Christ! On the sign, describe the characteristics of the Men of Self that Paul warned against. To the left of Paul, list what Paul told us to follow as Men of God.

The key to resisting the lure of the world's deceptions and distractions lies in that Truth above all truth, God's Holy Scriptures. To the right of the Bible, write down some of the names that you found for the Word of God in Psalm 119, as well as the two that Paul mentions in 2 Timothy. To the left, list how the Bible is useful or profitable to all disciples of Christ. On the cross, write the word for the Good News proclaimed in God's Word. Herein lies the power to endure persecution and stand firm as the people of the one true God!

Now that you have completed your Diagram, take a few moments to consider the full picture. Be sure to share your thoughts with your family during the **Family Bonfire** time this week.

A.C.T.S. PRAYER TIME

A - Adoration_____

C - Confession_____

T - Thanksgiving_____

S - Supplication_____

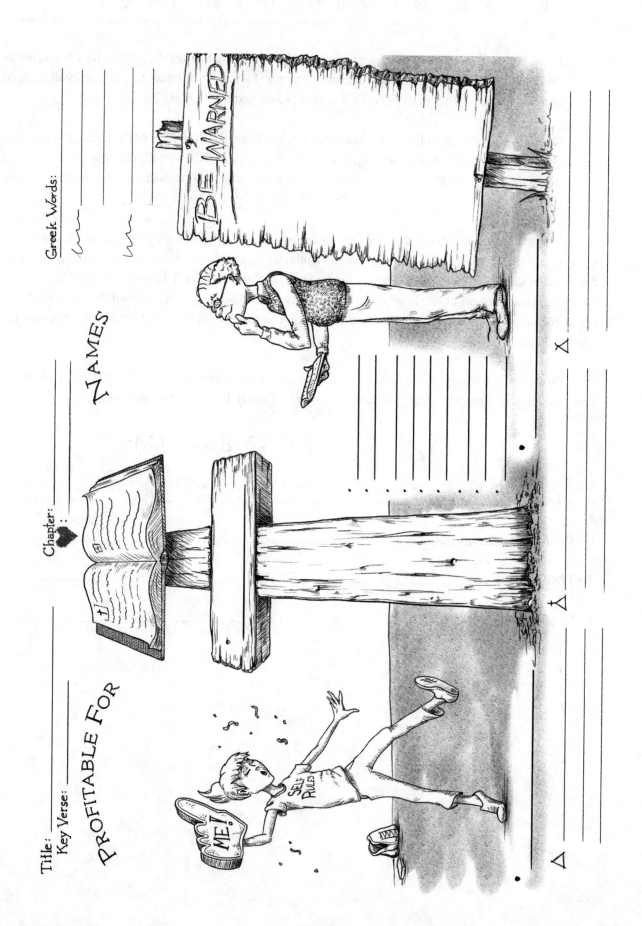

Title: _____

Key Verse: _____

PROFITABLE FOR

Chapter: _____ : _____

NAMES

Greek Words:

~ _____

~ _____

BE WARNED

SELF RULES

ME!

164

THE INCREDIBLES:
JIM AND ELISABETH ELLIOT

Today, a husband and wife share their amazing story. For the purpose of this interview, we've brought Jim back from heaven and Elisabeth (now elderly and infirm) back to health. Please welcome Jim and Elisabeth Elliot, although we might better call them "Mr. and Mrs. Incredible."

Jim: Mr. and Mrs. Incredible? I don't think so.

Elisabeth: We agree on that, Jim. Although I guess in some ways we are incredible.

J: What? I thought we agreed!

E: We do. I just know we are striving to be "good servants of Jesus Christ" (1 Timothy 4:6). So perhaps we're incredible after all.

J: I guess I see where you're coming from. Speaking of that, where did you come from, anyway?

E: I was born to missionary parents in Belgium in 1926. We moved to Pennsylvania when I was only a few months old. What about you, dear?

J: I guess you had a head start on me. I was born in 1927 in good old Portland, Oregon.

E: Were your parents missionaries too?

J: Not exactly. But they both walked with Christ and raised all four of us kids to know and love Him. In that way they had as large an influence as many missionaries.

E: The strong faith of our families prepared us to serve Him, didn't it?

J: Yes, indeed. And their dedication to missionary causes challenged and inspired us. We both enrolled at Wheaton College—where we met—and planned to prepare for mission service.

E: After we graduated, God used us on the mission field as single people.

J: Right again. I'd heard that there was one Christian worker for every 50,000 people overseas and one to every 500 in the United States. I wanted to change that ratio. We both served in Ecuador before marrying in 1953.

E: Yes, I went to work with the Colorado Indians. Later, I went to live with another missionary family and began to learn Quechua, the language you were learning.

J: I wanted you to learn the tribal languages before I weighed you down with the responsibilities of marriage.

E: (laughing) You were quite a responsibility!

J: But the Quechua were not the only people God had called us to reach.

E: You're right. For years, you sensed a deep call to the Auca ("savage," now known as the Waorani, "people") tribe. Their hostility kept most missionaries away.

J: Indeed. My friends and I had prayed for the Aucas for years. But we had much to learn.

E: Nothing could prepare us for jungle living except, well, jungle living!

J: You worked hard to make a home in such a primitive place. But our missionary friends faced the same challenges.

E: Yes, five young families worked together. You and I also worked to translate the New Testament into Quechua. We were still working on that when little Valerie was born in 1955.

J: But we were also working on "Operation Auca," our plan to reach this people group.

E: Yes. You men planned to fly over the Palm Beach area and drop gifts as a way to their trust.

J: And we did—for more than two months. They accepted our friendly offers. They even sent gifts back to us: a beaded headband, then a parrot.

E: The next step was staying there overnight. You and Roger went first, then the rest joined you in the crude tree house you made. Things seemed to be going well.

J: The fifth day, we saw a group of Auca men coming our way. We thought they wanted to greet us. Instead, they had come to kill us.

E: And you didn't resist because you had already agreed not to fight back.

J: Correct. If anything happened, we knew we'd go to heaven. But we hadn't yet reached the Aucas for Christ.

E: When the wives didn't hear back, we feared the worst. We spent the night and next day in prayer.

J: By that time, we were in God's presence. And your faithfulness meant many of the Aucas later came to faith.

E: At the time, I didn't feel faithful—only heartbroken. But God used several of us to help complete your mission. When Valerie and I returned to the States in 1963, some of the Aucas had already come to know Christ.

J: All because you were willing to forgive and to place His interests before your own. I believe our death has had a greater impact than our lives. And the books you've written have been a big part of that, my dear.

E: So you know about the books? I'm glad. God has used our stories to call many to the mission field.

J: I look forward to more conversations in heaven about that. See you there, Mrs. Incredible.

Jim Elliot, Nate Saint, Roger Youderian, Peter Fleming and Ed McCully all died at Palm Beach at the hands of the Waorani on January 8, 1956. Elisabeth's book, Through Gates of Splendor, gives the details of Operation Auca and the tragic deaths of the five young missionaries. The recent film The End of the Spear also tells their story.

DAY ONE

ON MY KNEES:

Good morning, front-row, first-seat student! Welcome back to another new week and our final chapter of 2 Timothy. Your faithful diligence is such sweet encouragement to the "Timothy's" around you. Carry on, we are praying for you.

Pray. "Lord, continue to give me a longing for Your Word today. Help me want to want to grow in Your wisdom more than that of the world's, my friends' or even my own. I want to know YOU more. Speak to me through Your words."

Write. Turn to a new page in the *"Write!"* portion of your Sword Study and write 2 Timothy 4:1-2.

Read. Turn from your well-read pages of Chapter 3 to Chapter 4 and read all 22 verses before beginning your study.

INVESTIGATIVE STUDY
STREETVIEW: CHAPTER 4

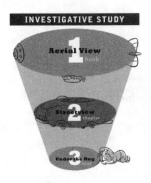

It doesn't seem possible that we have already arrived to this point, and yet, Chapter 1 seems so long ago! We will begin studying this chapter by interviewing verse sections. Open your Bible to 2 Timothy 4 and answer the following questions using the Word of God. Allow Scripture to answer for itself.

Apply!

Verse 1

Before what audience does Paul give his charge to Timothy?

_____

What does Paul highlight concerning Jesus?

_____

Verse 2

What are Paul's exhortations for Timothy in this verse?

_____ _____ _____ _____ _____

When is Timothy to be ready/instant/prepared?

_____

How is Timothy to exhort/encourage others?

_____

Verses 3-4

Who are "they" in these verses? (Hint: recall Chapter 3)

_____

What is said about the ears of the men?

_____

How do these men satisfy their dislike of hearing the Word of God taught strongly?

_____

What will be exchanged for truth?

_____

Verse 5

What list of "to-do's" does Paul give Timothy?

_____

Verses 6-8

What words does Paul give us as evidence that this letter may be his last?

_____

How does Paul describe his life in verse 6?

_____

What reward does Paul mention?

_____

Who receives this reward?

_____

Verses 9-15 and 19-21

How many people are listed in these verses?

_____

Does that sound like a lot?

_____

Should we wait until another day to focus on all of these people?

_____

We will wait until the end of the week to focus on the people Paul mentions.

Verses 16-18

How does Paul show his patience and love towards the body of Christ in verse 16?

_____

Who did not desert Paul?

_____

From what did the Lord deliver Paul ?

_____

What *did* the Lord do for Paul (17)?

_____

What was Paul certain that the Lord *would do* for him (18)?

_____

Verse 22

What does Paul pray for Timothy in this verse?

_____

How is it similar to what he prayed in the verses in Chapter 1?

_____

APPLY!

"In season and out of season"
What does this statement mean to you?
_____

What are some practical examples of being in season and out in your daily life?
(Such as being healthy/sick)
_____
_____
_____

How can you be prepared for either scenario?
_____

A.C.T.S. PRAYER TIME

A - *Adoration*_____

C - *Confession*_____

T - *Thanksgiving*_____

S - *Supplication*_____

D A Y   T W O

ON MY KNEES:

Are you on top of your game or under the weather? Either way, share your innermost feelings with the Lord openly. He is able to handle each one of our emotions. Go speak with Him through prayer.

Pray. "Father, You alone hear my thoughts, cries and feelings with unbiased ears and eternal patience. I want to deepen my relationship with You. Permanently impress Your words on my heart that I would leave my time greatly affected."

Write. Turn to your *"Write!"* section and write 2 Timothy 4:3-5.

Read. Before beginning your INVESTIGATIVE STUDY, read Chapter 4 of 2 Timothy.

Apply!

INVESTIGATIVE STUDY
STREETVIEW: CHAPTER 4

Did you wonder what Paul meant by some of the phrases that he used in this fourth chapter as you read it again today? Timothy knew Paul well. He had spent a great deal of time with him on the mission field, received previous letters, and been discipled by him for years when he received this letter. Paul could use some "shorthand" or references that he knew Timothy would understand, but that could leave us a bit lost.

Therefore, we are going to have Scripture help give us a better understanding by doing a couple, short cross reference exercises to help us interpret some mysterious phrases or words that Paul used. First, we will ask a question and then we will look up passages to help answer the question. Look up these verses and note any information that helps describe the word or phrase in the question.

What did Paul mean when he used the phrase "His appearing" in verse 1?

Look at the following passages and note what you learn.

1 Timothy 6:13-16

_____

Titus 2:11-14

_____

2 Timothy 4:8

_____

Paul was Jewish, so why did he mention only the Gentiles in verse 17?

Romans 1:8-17

_____

Acts 20:18-24*

_____

Acts 26:16-18

_____

Did it make a difference to Paul whether a man was Jew or Gentile?

_____

What lion's mouth was Paul speaking of in verse 17? The following verses use the same word. Was Paul describing a literal lion, or was he using an analogy?

1 Samuel 17:37

_____

Literal? Yes/No

Psalm 22:21

_____

Literal? Yes/No

As we look at this statement, verse 16 of 2 Timothy also helps us understand what Paul had escaped. The words "first defense" refer to his first time in front of the Roman officials. Do you recall what the punishment for crimes was during the Roman era? Often men and women suffered martyrdom. Thus, we can conclude that Paul was referring to a literal lion in 2 Timothy 4:17.

Even so, in 1 Peter 5:8, Peter tells us that there is another lion of which we should be aware. Note what you learn here:

_____

_____

_____

Paul says he is being "poured out like a drink offering" in 2 Timothy 4:6…what does that mean?

During Jewish sacrifices, a drink offering of wine was poured over the animal being sacrificed as a special offering to the Lord. Paul was saying that his life was being emptied of strength to the point of death. He had already said he was a living sacrifice and now his life was being poured out for Christ's sake as well. Look at the following references for additional examples of sacrifices, offerings and being "poured out."

Hebrews 10:10-12: _____

Romans 12:1-2: _____

Philippians 1:20-21: _____

Philippians 2:17: _____

Genesis 3:21 (Note: What was sacrificed and why? The entire chapter is helpful for context):

_____

"And now my life ebbs away; days of suffering grip me…." Job 30:16 states in the 1984 NIV. Giving up our will and living for Christ is our offering to Him. Some will find this too difficult, restraining or extravagant. As you live your life, it is likely that many will tell you that it is a waste to serve an unseen God. Do you know the story of Mary's offering in John 12:2-4? Those around her considered her foolish, but the Lord considered her offering as a priceless, gift of worship.

APPLY!

How can you test your motives? What is most important to you in the games you play? Is it the prize or fame or potential scholarship? What is most important to you in the Bible Bee? Focusing on the temporal rewards quickly surpasses the eternal goal of obedience to God's ways if we are not constantly seeking to check our hearts against the truth. Think about how you compete. Honestly assess the following aspects.

My reaction when I don't do well:
_____

My reaction when I do awesomely:
_____

My treatment of fellow competitors:
_____

The amount of time I am involved (circle one):   Over-the-Top   Balanced   Apathetic

A.C.T.S. PRAYER TIME

Close by looking at Proverb 24:12 and going to the Lord in prayer.

A - *Adoration* _____

C - *Confession* _____

T - *Thanksgiving* _____

S - *Supplication* _____

DIGGING DEEPER

In order to truly understand why Paul describes his life as a drink offering, we need to take a short look at the Jewish history of offerings. The Jewish person of the day would have readily understood why he said this and we need to set his words against the same backdrop. We won't go in great depth, just enough to understand the significance of his comparison.

There are six main Jewish offerings. The book of Leviticus depicts many of them in detail. We can learn of the days and times they were offered as well as the ceremonies that surrounded them. Below is a simple chart of offerings which gives you a brief purpose, the elements, cross references and representation for each offering. [7]

Name	Purpose	Elements	Cross Reference	Representation
Burnt Offering	Voluntary; atonement for unintentional sin in general. Shows devotion, commitment and surrender to God	Bull, ram, dove (or pigeon for the poor)	Leviticus 1; 6:8-13; 8:18-21; 16:24	Jesus' death as achieving the will of God. Christ's death glorified God.
Grain (meal) Offering	Voluntary; recognized God's goodness and provision. Shows devotion to God.	Grain, fine flour, olive oil, incense, baked bread, salt; no yeast or honey; accompanied burnt offering and peace offering (along with drink offering)	Leviticus 2; 6:14-23	Christ as perfect Man in perfect obedience from birth to death at Calvary. Christ's obedience pleased God.
Peace Offering	Voluntary, thanksgiving and fellowship, (communal meal), included vow, thanksgiving and freewill offerings.	Any animal without defect from herd or flock; variety of breads	Leviticus 3; 7:11-34	Christ as the One who has, through His death and resurrection, reconciled God and man. Christ's death allows man's fellowship with God.
Sin Offering	Mandatory atonement for specific unintentional sin; confession of sin; forgiveness of sin; cleansing	Ranged from a young bull (for High Priest and whole congregation), goats, lambs, or a dove to 1/10 ephah of fine flour	Leviticus 4; 5:1-13; 6:24-30; 8:14-17; 16:3-22	Christ as the propitiation for our sin as he bore our sins. His suffering for our sins reconciled us with God, as the One and only holy, righteous God.
Trespass Offering	Mandatory atonement for unintentional sin requiring restitution; payment of 20% fine.	Ram	Leviticus 5:14-19; 6:1-7; 7:1-6	Death of Christ in covering our needs when we commit sins as believers. Christ is our Advocate before God as he compensates for any offence or injury sin has caused God in our daily relationship
Drink Offering	Accompanied other offerings;	Strong wine – poured over other offerings.	Genesis 35:14; Leviticus 23, I Chronicles 29:21; 2 Kings 16:13,15; Ezra 7:17	Christ in his perfection due to work he accomplished, brought joy to God for all Jesus had done. Never consumed by offender.

(Portions of this chart have been extracted from the NIV Study Bible and Andrew Langham's Article at http://www.biblecentre.org/topics/al_drink_offering.htm)

DAY THREE

ON MY KNEES:

Briefly glance around at your surroundings. You are definitely blessed. The Lord has cared for you and you have, at the very least, your own copy of His Word. Go to Him in grateful adoration.

Pray. "Heavenly Father, I admit that I can get wrapped up in the things I don't have or that I want. I lose sight of all that You have provided. I want to be ready in season and out to answer Your call. Thank You for all Your graciousness and mercy."

Write. 2 Timothy 4:6-8

Read. Once again, please read Chapter 4 of 2 Timothy.

INVESTIGATIVE STUDY
STREETVIEW: CHAPTER 4

Crown of Righteousness…what is this about?

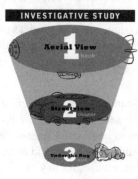

Apply!

The word *crown*, used in 2 Timothy 4:6, literally means "surrounding" and was talked about during Paul's time as a wreath or the garland that was presented to the winners of athletic games. Military victors and dignitaries would also wear them. It was a great honor to be wearing a crown of this type. Here are a few uses of the word "crown" in the Bible. Note the type of crown, who receives it and when they receive it on the lines after the reference.

Job 19:6-9:_____

Psalm 8:4-6: _____

Psalm 149:4 _____

Proverbs 16:31 _____

Proverbs 17:6 _____

1 Corinthians 9:25 _____

Matthew 27:27-29 _____

Hebrews 2:9 _____

James 1:12 _____

1 Peter 5:4 _____

Revelation 2:10 _____

APPLY!

Offerings... What about tithing? Isn't it interesting that we sometimes interchange these two words?

How are they similar? _____

How are they different? _____

Do you give tithes or offerings? _____

What does the Lord expect? _____

Here are a few passages about the subject, if you have a few moments today or later in the week:

Deuteronomy 14:21-24 _____

Malachi 3:7-11 _____

Matthew 23:22-24 _____

Luke 18:11-13 _____

Hebrews 7:7-10 _____

A.C.T.S. PRAYER TIME

A - Adoration_____

C - Confession_____

T - Thanksgiving_____

S - Supplication_____

"God is God. Because He is God, He is worthy of my trust and obedience.
I will find rest nowhere but in His holy will that is unspeakably
beyond my largest notions of what he is up to."
~Elisabeth Elliot~

DAY FOUR

ON MY KNEES:

As you return here to study each day, you are compared to the wise man who builds on the rock. Not only are you hearing God's Word, but your action of returning to His feet for more wisdom is the doing of the Word. Let's pray that we would continue to not just be hearers, but doers of the Word.

Pray. "Jesus, this was Your truth as you spoke to Your disciples. I don't want to be like the foolish man who only hears and then goes on with his life in "status quo" mode. Remind me of what I have learned by prompting me throughout my days by the work of Your Holy Spirit. "

Write. Turn to the pages behind your *"Write!"* tab and copy 2 Timothy 4:9-10.

Read. Once again, read 2 Timothy 4.

INVESTIGATIVE STUDY
LISTS & DEFINITIONS

Apply!

Today's overview of Chapter 4 involves looking at the five lists that Paul uses. Fill in the list outline below as you read through the chapter. Don't miss adding the definitions to the less-used words in letters C, D and E. If there are other words that spark your curiosity, look those up as well.

The Lists of Chapter 4

List #1 Paul charges Timothy to do what...

A. _____

B. _____

C. _____

D. _____

E. _____

How... i. _____

How... ii. _____

Add definitions to letters C, D and E.

List #2 What the Men of Self will & will not do…

A. _____

B. _____

C. _____

D. _____

E. _____

List #3 When the Men of Self do "List #2", then you will do this…

A. _____

B. _____

C. _____

D. _____

**List #4 For I, Paul, have done this as I am now being poured
out as a drink offering for you…**

A. _____

B. _____

C. _____

We must stop for a brief moment and note the incredible connection between this list in 2 Timothy 4:7 and the three examples in 2 Timothy 2:4-6. Do you see any connection between these things and 2 Timothy 2:4-6? Describe what you notice here:

_____

_____

List #5 Everyone has left me, but the Lord hasn't! He has …

A. _____

B. _____

C. _____

And He will also….

A. _____

B. _____

Look over the simplicity of this chapter when it is written in list format. Do you see a hidden structure when it is written this way? Notice how Paul seems to be summarizing each of his previous chapters in order, starting with the first list and finally concluding with the third list (for third chapter). The final two lists summarize the fourth chapter by saying, "I have been your example" (list 4) and "God has sustained me thus far (list 5a) and I am confident He will in the end (list 5b)".

Before we conclude today, quickly skim back over the chapter and mark any references to God as well as any key words that you find.

APPLY!

Let's go back to that "being ready in season or out of season" phrase within 2 Timothy 4:2. A very practical way that we can do this in our lives today is in the aspect of how we handle our finances. No matter our age, we can be used of the Lord if we are ready. Think through your own finances. How do you use your funds? Do you tithe? Look up Luke 12:47-49.

A.C.T.S. PRAYER TIME

A - *Adoration*_____

C - *Confession*_____

T - *Thanksgiving*_____

S - *Supplication*_____

D A Y   F I V E

ON MY KNEES:

You are here. The Lord waits as you prepare and decide how much you want to be here. Do you come with a grumbling heart wondering how long this lesson will be? Do you come rejoicing? How incredible is it to ponder that you choose how you will come to Him, and the God of the universe waits on you - how humbling! Let's pray.

Pray. "Lord, thank You for making it possible for me to sit at Your feet and learn from You. Open my heart to Your Word now as I come to You."

Write. Grab your pen or pencil and begin to write 2 Timothy 4:11-12 in the *"Write!"* section of your Sword Study.

Read. Be creative. Come up with a different approach to reading through Chapter 4 of 2 Timothy today.

INVESTIGATIVE STUDY
STREETVIEW: CHAPTER 4

Apply!

As we conclude the STREETVIEW of Chapter 4 and do word studies of the key words, we return to the substantial number of people that Paul has mentioned. First, we will list the people and add a short note regarding what Paul said about them. Also, mark "for" or "against" next to each person/people depending on whether they stuck with Paul or deserted him. Fill in the lines below.

Person	**Summary**	**For/Against**
_____	_____	_____
_____	_____	_____
_____	_____	_____
_____	_____	_____
_____	_____	_____

Person	Summary	For/Against
_____	_____	_____
_____	_____	_____
_____	_____	_____
_____	_____	_____
_____	_____	_____
_____	_____	_____
_____	_____	_____
_____	_____	_____
_____	_____	_____
_____	_____	_____

Here we see Paul as a relational person. He has been a leader of the early church. Suddenly, he is alone with the exception of "only" Luke. Once again, he describes the desertion of some friends in Christ and even mentions one person to watch out for because of the harm he had caused Paul. Being persecuted for the sake of Christ is not just physical, but often consists of great emotional and relational difficulty and pain. Paul is lonely. He has been hurt by the very people whom He lovingly led. He desires to have Timothy visit him and experience the joy of his fellowship (1:4) as well as Mark's. As he closes his letter, he ends with a reminder to come quickly before winter.

"Paul did not write this section as an afterthought; it was not incidental but vital to the Spirit-inspired message. The Lord wanted the rest of His church to know about these people in Paul's life and to learn from their faithfulness or their failure." [5]

Our God is relational as well. He desires a deep love relationship with us. He also gives us gifts of like-minded friendships to encourage us. When we experience hardship or loneliness, part of the perseverance is learning to lean on the One who is always with us, for we are never alone.

APPLY!

Find and read Job 6:14-21*. Take to heart the type of friend you are to others. We must be strong in the Word, proclaiming the gospel and willing to stand in faithfulness. We need to encourage our friends towards the same.

A.C.T.S. PRAYER TIME

A - *Adoration* _____

C - *Confession* _____

T - *Thanksgiving* _____

S - *Supplication* _____

NO EXCUSE:
AMY CARMICHAEL

Excuses. We're good at making them, aren't we? From "The dog ate my homework" to "He hit me first," we all find times and reasons to make excuses for not doing what we should.

When God called Moses, Israel's future leader had plenty of excuses. He wasn't the man for the job (Exodus 3:11). The people might not believe or listen (Exodus 4:1). He wasn't much of a speaker anyway (Exodus 4:10). But somehow, God countered all his excuses and used Moses to lead an entire nation out of Egypt.

When God called young Amy Carmichael to be a missionary, she—like Moses—could have offered excuses. The eldest daughter of a wealthy Irish family, she lost her father to death during her teenage years. Before long, her family ran out of money, and Amy had to drop out of boarding school to help her mother with the younger children. No money, interrupted education—those sound like good excuses, don't they?

But Amy had another excuse: her health. She suffered from neuralgia, a nerve disease that causes chronic pain and fatigue. She had begun a ministry with the "shawlies" (girls who worked in the mills), but her volunteer work seemed to make her illness worse. She knew she must stop her ministry. How could someone in such poor health even consider going to the mission field?

But God
When Moses offered excuses, God had answers. And in Amy's case, He had answers ready, too. When Amy prayed about her health and her calling, she heard His voice: "Go."

"Surely, Lord, you don't mean it," she told Him.

Again, He urged her, "Go."

But what would her mother say? God took care of that, too. When Amy asked about going to the mission field to serve, her mother said God had already made it clear: she must let Amy go.

Amy had no more excuses.

Or did she? For more than a year, she attempted to find a place to serve, but no one wanted her. Had she misunderstood God's call?

In 1892, Amy sent a letter to Japan and offered to help those serving there. Early the next year, she sailed for Japan with three other missionary women.

Amy didn't wait to begin her missionary service until the ship reached Japan. On the long, difficult journey, she won the captain to Christ. And during her brief stay in Japan, her devotion to God and the Japanese people brought many more to the Savior.

After only fifteen months on the field, Amy became seriously ill. In 1892, she returned to England for treatment. Would her poor health become an excuse to stay home?

Of course not! The next year, Amy sailed to the mission field again—this time, to India. She hoped the climate would improve her health, but she also prayed for countless souls to be won to the Lord.

Dohnavur

In India, many more excuses awaited Amy. Too hot, too dirty, too difficult, too dangerous, too many cultural differences—any of these could have kept her from serving. But she chose to fulfill her calling instead. In the process, God opened her eyes to a terrible problem among India's young girls. Many were being kidnapped, held against their wills in the Hindu temples, and hurt in unspeakable ways.

Amy made it her mission to rescue these girls and help them build new lives. She founded Dohnavur Fellowship as a safe haven where the girls could receive a home, an education, good food and medical care, and—most important of all—the good news of Jesus Christ. She loved and cared for the Dohnavur girls as her own. To mark her important place in their lives, they called her "Amma" (mother).

In 1931, Amy fell and suffered an injury that left her bedridden for the rest of her life. But no-excuse Amy's ministry continued. She began writing books (thirty-five in all) that told about India, her life in Christ, and the lives of the rescued children. She died at the age of eighty-three, still serving and caring for her Indian children.

"One can give without loving, but one cannot love without giving," Amy said. As her life proves, when it comes to following Christ and serving His people, excuses don't matter. Love does.

DAY ONE

ON MY KNEES:

"Do you not know? Have you not heard? The everlasting God, Lord, the Creator of the ends of the earth does not become weary or tired. His understanding is inscrutable. He gives strength to the weary. And to him who lacks might He increases power." Isaiah 40:28-29 (NASB)

Pray. "Lord, I have heard, I do know You are the everlasting God, Creator of all things. I do become weary and want to depend on your strength in my time of need. Increase my endurance, even today as I begin my study. In Your powerful Name, I ask. Amen."

Write. As you write 2 Timothy 4:13-15, consider the state Paul was in when he penned the words. Praise the Lord for the wonderful, blessings of your home as you write.

Read. Please re-read 2 Timothy 4.

INVESTIGATIVE STUDY
PREACH *WORD STUDY*

Apply!

Paul uses the words *preach, preacher* and *preaching* in 2 Timothy. As we come to his final chapter, he solemnly charges Timothy in the presence of God and Christ to PREACH the Word. Since he has focused on it previously, he has just dwelled on the *Scriptures* and seems to highlight its importance in Chapter 4, we have chosen it as one of our last word studies.

PART A: As we look up the words *preaching, preach* and *preacher* in the Strong's Concordance, we find that the Strong's numbers assigned to them in 2 Timothy are 2782, 2783 and 2784. Note this, because they will be used to look up a detailed explanation of the Greek words in Part B. Below is the transliteration, the pronunciation, and then the basic definition from the Strong's lexicon.

2782. *kerugma* *kay-roog-mah*; (from 2784); a proclamation, especially of the gospel. (*preaching;* 2 Timothy 4:17)

2783. *kērusso*; *kay-roos-so;* to herald, as a public crier, especially divine truth, gospel. Proclaim; publish, not just a profession (*preacher;* 2 Timothy 4:2)

2784. *kērux*, *kay-roox* ; (from 2784); a herald of divine truth; especially the gospel (*preach*; 2 Timothy 1:11)

PART B: We will now look up the numbers 2782, 2783 and 2784 in another Greek lexicon to discover a more detailed explanation of the words *preaching, preach* and *preacher* in Greek:

2782. to preach, cry out, proclaim. Sermon, message, proclamation of the redeeming purpose of God in Christ.

2783. to preach. Herald, crier, proclaimer, preacher. Word denotes one who is employed by God in the work of proclaiming salvation. In 2 Timothy 1:11, the word is conjoined with teacher.

2784. to preach, to herald, proclaim. Especially to preach, publish, or announce religious truth, the gospel with its attendant privileges and obligations.

PART C: We are going to primarily look at the word in 2 Timothy 4:2, which is 2784 and other passages that use the same form of the Greek word. Before we do this, we will finish today in the 2 Timothy verses alone.

Turn to 2 Timothy 1:10-11.

Why was Paul *preaching* in this verse?

_____

What was he *preaching*?

_____

Turn to 2 Timothy 4:2.

Who was to *preach*?

_____

What was he to *preach*?

_____

What two words are synonyms between verse 2 and 3?

_____

Turn to 2 Timothy 4:17.

What word is used here for *preach* in your version?

_____

Who *preached* in this verse?

_____

Who strengthened him?

_____

Who was the audience?

_____

Our prayer is that you fully understand that the words used here are not exclusive to today's profession of "preacher" or pastor. We are all called to stand on the Word and proclaim it boldly to the lost world and encourage fellow believers to walk in its ways through our words and living it.

APPLY!

Have you ever gone to a big city and seen a person on the street corner with posters hung from their neck proclaiming the end of the world or "Repent and Be Saved!" In all likelihood, they launched their campaign due to a conviction of the many places we are commanded to herald, cry out and proclaim the Word of God.

Can you think of any others who might be doing the same type of campaign for another area of the Word of God?_____

What are other ways that people announce what they believe?

_____

In what ways would the Lord like you to personally proclaim His truth?

_____

A.C.T.S. PRAYER TIME

**A - *Adoration*_____

**C - *Confession*_____

**T - *Thanksgiving*_____

**S - *Supplication*_____

DIGGING DEEPER

If you have extra time, take a moment and investigate the "Day of Prayer" or "Meet Me at the Pole" websites.

DAY TWO

INVESTIGATIVE STUDY
PREACH CROSS REFERENCES

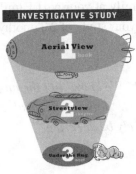

Apply!

"Preach, Timothy, preach! Proclaim all that I have taught you, especially the gospel!" The scarlet thread that runs through the Scriptures is the proclamation of Christ as our Savior, and after redemption, how we are to live under His Lordship. Find the passages listed below and summarize all that you learn about preaching/proclaiming the Word and the gospel.

Acts 10:42-43* _____

1 Corinthians 9:24-27* _____

_____

Matthew 26:11-13 _____

_____

Colossians 1:23 _____

_____

1 Corinthians 15:12-14 _____

_____

Mark 1:14 _____
_____

Acts 5:40-42 _____
_____

1 Corinthians 2:1 _____
_____

Colossians 4:2-5 _____
_____

1 John 1:2-4 _____
_____

Be encouraged, modern-day "Timothy!" As you study the Scriptures, know that they are inspired by the God of all ages and are valuable for teaching sound doctrine, reproof, correction and maturing in godliness. Charge!

APPLY!

Create an outline for a short, 3 to 5 minute sermon to deliver to your family at your next Family Bonfire. Focus on a topic you have been particularly interested in during your study of 2 Timothy.

"We are not asked to SEE," said Amy. "Why need we when we KNOW?" We know--not the answer to the inevitable Why, but the incontestable fact that it is for the best. "It is an irreparable loss, but is it faith at all if it is 'hard to trust' when things are entirely bewildering?"
Amy Carmichael

A.C.T.S. PRAYER TIME

A - Adoration _____

C - Confession _____

T - Thanksgiving _____

S - Supplication _____

DAY THREE

ON MY KNEES:

The words of the Bible will be a lamp unto your feet for years to come. They will be a light unto your path. As the world darkens, your time in the Word will light your ways and help you to be a light to others. Commit your ways to Him! Let's pray.

Pray. "Jesus, You are the Morning Star. You are the Light of the World. I want to glorify You and be a reflection of Your glory. Help me learn how to do that in new ways today. Lord, also give me the endurance and perseverance for the hard work it takes to rightly divide Your Word. You never promised that it would be easy to become Your workman! In Your name, I pray. Amen."

Write. Please write 2 Timothy 4:18-19 in the pages of your *"Write!"* section.

Read. Before you begin your Greek word study, please read Chapter 4 of 2 Timothy.

INVESTIGATIVE STUDY
PATIENCE - WORD STUDY

Apply!

"Come on!" "Let's get moving!"
"How much L – O – N – G – E – R ?"

You have probably heard these and other statements which display a lack of patience. We have been told over and over how we are a generation of impatience because we have so much convenience, such as fast food restaurants, high speed internet and Siri or Google. We don't want to wait and we don't expect to wait. The question is, "Is patience just a matter of waiting?"

Paul has mentioned *patience* several times in 2 Timothy and while it doesn't seem to be a word that qualifies as one of the top key words, it becomes a contender when Paul ties it with his summarizing charge.

Look up and read 2 Timothy 4:1-2. How are we to do all the items in verse 2? _____

_____

Look up and read 2 Timothy 2:24.

When are we to be *patient* according to this passage? _____

_____

Look up and read 2 Timothy 3:10.

Who exhibited *patience* in the passage? _____

What are we to do with *patience* according to him? _____

_____

Paul uses three different Greek words for the three instances he uses the words related to *patience*. His uses are not simply different forms of the same root word. Today, merely read the three word studies for *anexikakos, makrothumia* and *hupomone* and the short questions around 2 Timothy. We will continue with cross references tomorrow.

Word Study:

Patient, 2 Timothy 2:24

PART A: The Strong's Concordance number assigned to *patient* is 420.

420. *anexikakos, (an-ex-ik-ak-ōs),* from 430 and 2556; enduring, put up with, bear under ill, bad, evil, harm, noisome, wicked

PART B: Now, we look up the number 420 in another Greek lexicon to discover a more detailed explanation of the word *patient* in Greek:

> 1) to bear bad, describing one who bears evil, sorrow, ill. (Only occurrence of this word in the entire Bible is 2 Timothy 2:24!)

Long Suffering/Patience, 2 Timothy 4:2

PART A: The Strong's Concordance number assigned to *patient* is 3115.

3115. *makrothumia,* (*mak-roth-oo-mee-ah*), from the same as 3116, fortitude, forbearance, long-suffering, with long temper.

PART B: Now, we look up the number 3115 in another Greek lexicon to discover a more detailed explanation for the word *long-suffering/patience* in Greek:

> 1) to be long-suffering, forbearance, self-restraint before proceeding to action.
> 2) a person who is able to avenge himself yet refrains from doing so.

Patience, 2 Timothy 3:10

PART A: The Strong's Concordance number assigned to *patience* is 5281.

5281. *hupomone*, (*hoop-om-on-ay*), from 5278 cheerful or hopeful endurance, consistency, enduring, waiting. Stay under, bear, suffer trials or suffering (patience)

PART B: Now, we look up the number 5278 in another Greek lexicon to discover a more detailed explanation for the word *patience* in Greek:

1) to persevere, remain under, a bearing up under, endurance as to things or circumstances. This is in contrast to endurance towards people.

2) generally meaning endurance, perseverance or constancy under suffering in faith and duty. Specifically patience as a quality of mind, the bearing of evils and suffering with a tranquil mind.

PART C: Write each of the verses below and insert one of the above phases from PART B, 2) in place of the word *patient*.

2 Timothy 2:24:

_____

_____

_____

2 Timothy 3:10:

_____

_____

_____

2 Timothy 4:2:

_____

_____

_____

* Note: All word studies use Strong's Concordance, which is keyed on the King James Version. For example, in the KJV, the word makrothumia is translated, "longsuffering", while other versions translated it as, "patience".
In addition, verses such as 2 Timothy 3:10, which have lists of English words, can have the same English word applied to two different Greek words in the various translations. The English word, "patience" appears in the NASB, ESV, and NIV as the second-to-last word in the series, while it appears as the last word in the series in the KJV.

APPLY!

What tests your patience? List the top three things that test your patience:

_____   _____   _____

Who tests your patience? List the top three people who test your patience:

_____   _____   _____

How can you plan to handle your lack of patience better?

_____

_____

Use your closing prayer time to seek the Lord concerning your patience…or lack thereof.

A.C.T.S. PRAYER TIME

A - Adoration_____

C - Confession_____

T - Thanksgiving_____

S - Supplication_____

"I will not be satisfied.
I will not let my passion be held in a bottle.
I will not let my light be hidden.

I will stand up.
I will let my voice be heard.
I will lead. I will serve. I will fight.
I will tell people about Christ.
I will unsheathe my sword.

It's time to raise a revolution.
God will give me the strength."

~BJ Higgins, 1989-2005~

D A Y   F O U R

ON MY KNEES:

Soldier. Athlete. Farmer. Vacationer. Which one of these things doesn't belong with the others? While there are certainly times for physical rest, the concept of vacationing from the study of God's Word cannot be found in Scripture. Be encouraged, fellow worker, you are diligently doing the right thing and God will bless your efforts.

Pray. "Lord, help me to have the right heart attitude, as I come to do my Sword Study. Break the hardened areas of my heart where I am proud. Mold me, refine me and teach me in Your ways so that I might truly be the workman that You desire me to become. Thank you for encouraging me even when I don't perform perfectly"

Write. The words of 2 Timothy 4:20-22 will be the last ones that you write into your copy of 2 Timothy. Well done, conscientious writer!

Read. Open your Bible to 2 Timothy 4 and read all 22 verses.

INVESTIGATIVE STUDY
PATIENCE - CROSS REFERENCES

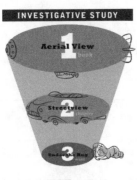

Apply!

Did you fill in some ways that you could better handle the areas that you lack *patience* with Bible passages? Our hope is that today's cross references will call us to the Lord's understanding and therefore ways to handle *patience* with our circumstances and with friend or foe. Find the passages listed below and summarize what you learn. (There are a variety of word uses for *patience* in translations, be sure to look for synonyms.)

1 Peter 2:20 _____

2 Peter 3:9 _____

Romans 2:4 _____

Proverbs 24:29-34* _____

Colossians 3:12-13 _____

Ephesians 4:1-6 _____

Colossians 1:10-12 _____

Hebrews 6:10-12 _____

James 1:3 _____

James 5:9-11 _____

Jeremiah 15:15 _____

2 Corinthians 6:2-10 _____

APPLY!

Plan a special time with your "Paul." Share a meal and fellowship (true fellowship is all about what the Lord has done, is doing and looks to be doing in your life) together. If you are blessed with several Paul's, take time for each one.

Plan a special time with a few of your "Timothy's." Be creative and think through what would be especially encouraging to them.

These events don't have to be costly or lengthy – just purposeful.

A.C.T.S. PRAYER TIME

A - *Adoration* _____

C - *Confession* _____

T - *Thanksgiving* _____

S - *Supplication* _____

"Satan is so much more in earnest than we are–he buys up the opportunity
while we are wondering how much it will cost."
~Amy Carmichael~

D A Y   F I V E

ON MY KNEES:

You have been faithful in much, and have endured through attacks and distractions. The enemy has been as a roaring lion, frustrated with a lost catch. You have done well through the Lord's strength. Begin once again in prayer.

Pray. Thank You, Lord, for each day that you have strengthened me to draw near to You. The more that I learn about You, the more that I love You and desire to walk faithfully with You. Open my eyes to the truth You wish to share with me today.

Write. Take a few minutes to review Chapter 4. Are there any references to God? Mark them with the appropriate symbols.

Read. Pull up your boot straps and read through the entire book of 2 Timothy before moving to your last "Day 10 Diagram".

INVESTIGATIVE STUDY
1-2-3 CHAPTER 4 – SUMMARIZE!

INVESTIGATIVE STUDY

1 Aerial View book

2 Streetview

3 Under the Rug

Apply!

Chapter 4 Summary:

We have arrived to another *"Day 10 Diagram"*.

Remember, if you have any problems figuring out how to fill in your *Day 10 Diagram*, talk to a parent; the Parent Guidebook includes the key to this diagram.

☐ To begin, look at the top of the *Day 10 Diagram*. Fill in the chapter number and the title that you created for this chapter.

☐ Next, which verse from the chapter do you think was the "key verse?"

☐ Beside the heart, list the references to any Bible passages that you have hidden your heart during your study of Chapter 4.

☐ On the right of the page, transfer your key Greek words from this chapter and write a shortened definition of their meanings.

On the bottom of the *Diagram* page, transfer the most important things that you learned

☐ about God through marking the references about Him in your Write! Tab. If you run out of space, continue on the back side of your Diagram.

Congratulations, young Timothy, for staying in the race through the end of this Sword Study! May you continue just as faithfully in the ongoing course that God has set for you in life for His glory and the benefit of His Kingdom!

Paul concludes his letter by reflecting on his own race which has wound down to its final steps; he knows that his life has served as a drink offering to the Lord for the benefit of many young Timothy's in the world. Even while in chains in a Roman prison, he rejoices that he has won a great victory in what truly counts- spreading the gospel for the sake of Christ!

In the Diagram, view our faithful followers of Christ on the victors' stands wearing their crowns of righteousness. In the boxes under the victors, mark each of the three verbs from 2 Timothy 4:7 that Paul uses to sum up his service to Jesus. In the two additional spaces under Paul, list what Paul has been (vs. 6) and what he will receive (vs. 8).

Throughout his marathon of servanthood, some co-workers in Christ remained steadfast alongside of Paul, while others fell away. List those whom he said stood firm for Christ in the "For" side of the grandstand, and those who turned away in the "Against" section. Paul charges Timothy to continue on toward his own victory; on the "Charge" banner, label Paul's nine instructions to Timothy as he closes out the letter. May we all strive in the Lord's mighty power to be obedient and cheerful servants in all that He commands.

Now that you have completed your Diagram, take a few moments to consider the full picture. Be sure to share your thoughts with your family during the **Family Bonfire** time this week.

A.C.T.S. PRAYER TIME

A - Adoration_____

C - Confession_____

T - Thanksgiving_____

S - Supplication_____

Title: _____

Key Verse: _____

Chapter: _____

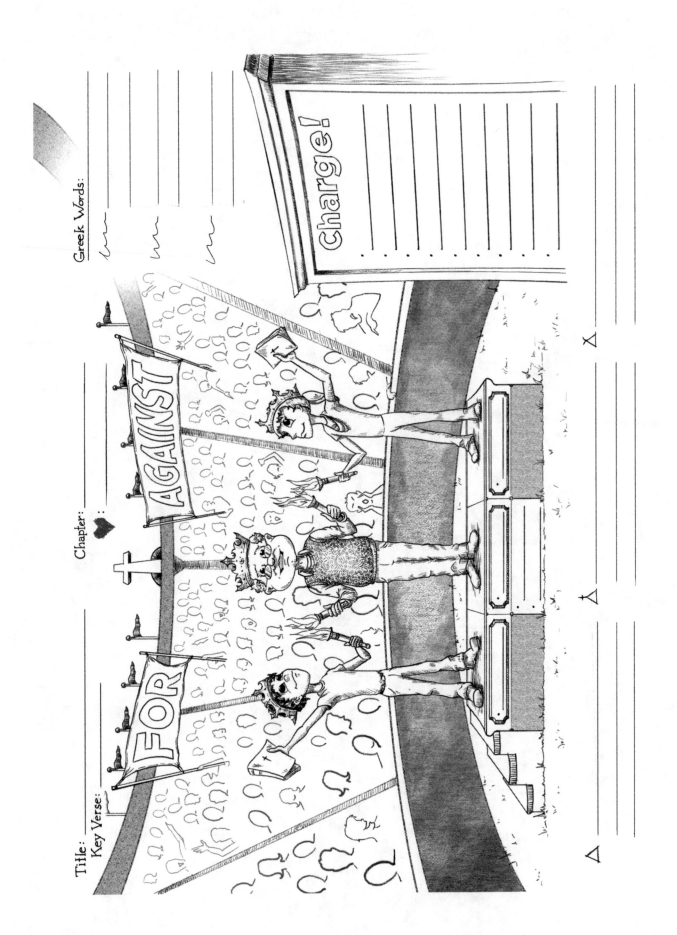

MORE FROM THE APOSTLE PAUL

Dear Friends,

Thank you for your diligence in completing this study. I applaud your efforts as good soldiers in Christ Jesus.

I return to these pages to introduce to you one final hero, a man dear to my heart. I wanted to tell you about him myself because he's from your own era.

In the not-quite-sixteen years BJ Higgins spent on this earth, he lived more than most people. This young man made consistent choices to put God's desires above his own. And God is using—and will continue to use—his story.

As a young boy, BJ showed an unusual interest in spiritual things. He wanted to talk about what he learned at church. He kept journals and wrote down ideas of Scriptures he wanted to study. When he was almost six years old, he prayed to receive Christ under his dad's direction.

One problem: BJ wasn't being real. His parents and older sisters had already accepted Christ, and he wanted to do the same. But God wouldn't let BJ rest in this false relationship. He wanted more. He wanted it all.

When BJ was in third grade, he heard a speaker named Afshin Zhiafat, a converted Muslim. That settled it. There would be no more faking for BJ Higgins.

From that day forward, BJ moved into ministry. As a second or third grader, he gave a neighbor boy an overview of the entire Bible and led him to Christ. BJ viewed his relationships and school assignments as vehicles for the gospel. A middle school classmate remembers,

Brent [BJ] did his report on the Left Behind series, and in doing so, shared the gospel to a group of seventh graders . . .

I remember thinking, "HE HAS WHAT I'M LOOKING FOR!! That is so cool he can be so bold."—Kara Palmer, blog posting at www.prayforbj.com

But BJ's biggest challenges lay ahead. During his eighth grade year, he accompanied his father to church one weekend. His sister Whitney and a team of other high school students were practicing a drama they planned to use to present the gospel on a mission trip to Ukraine.

BJ, according to the church's guidelines, wasn't old enough to make the trip. But he had a divine appointment in Peru.

In a few short weeks, BJ raised all the money needed for a five-week mission trip there. Awe Star staffer David Post, who trained Whitney's team, had observed BJ's passion and invited him to go. The smallest, youngest member of Awe Star's 2004 Peru team soon became known as its spiritual leader.

Not only did BJ have an impact on his team, but the trip had a huge impact on him. Awe Star teaching emphasizes a rite of passage, a definite step between childhood and adulthood. BJ embraced this teaching with all his heart. After five weeks of praying, giving his testimony, and leading people to Christ, BJ returned to his Indiana home committed to live as an adult—and serve as a missionary everywhere he went.

The next summer, intrigued by the possibility of a mission trip to Thailand, BJ almost didn't return to Peru. But his parents' prayers about Thailand never brought peace. BJ soon agreed with his family and returned to Peru. If the previous summer was life-changing, this one was incredible. As the Knightmare (Satan figure) in Awe Star's "Freedom" drama, BJ experienced both tremendous spiritual attack and tremendous victory. At God's prompting, he walked across a plaza to face four stern-faced policemen:

I [was] kinda nervous because they could've easily laughed in my face or else whipped out their uzis and ordered us to get off the premises, but God is teaching me obedience, so I went and talked to them. . . all four of them accepted Christ.—BJ's missionary journal

Within days of his return from Peru, everything changed. Everything, that is, except BJ's commitment to Christ. Read his passionate declaration, posted on his family's www.prayforbj.com blog during the six-week hospitalization that ended with his promotion to heaven:

I will not be satisfied.
I will not let my mission be held in a bottle.
I will not let my light be hidden.
I will stand up.
I will let my voice be heard.
I will lead. I will serve. I will fight.
I will tell people about Christ.
I will unsheathe my sword.
It's time to raise a revolution.

GOD WILL GIVE ME THE STRENGTH.—written by BJ Higgins and adopted by Awe Star Ministries as its Global Passage Creed

My friends, I regard you as I did young Timothy: ready in season and out. I beg you to allow the Word to do its work. Don't allow your study of Scripture to end with this Sword Study. Don't allow your light to be hidden.

It's time to raise a revolution. God will give you the strength.

Grace be with you,

Paul

Read more about BJ Higgins in the best-selling book I Would Die for You: One Student's Story of Passion, Service, and Faith (Revell, 2008), on his parents' blog, www.prayforbj.com, or via Awe Star Ministries, www.awestar.org.

DAY ONE

ON MY KNEES:

Well done, you have been a faithful student of the Word of God! This week we go back up to the AERIAL VIEW to review each of the chapters of 2 Timothy. We will use this week to cement all we have learned by reading our own prayers, reading through the chapters once more and looking back at each chapter's "Day 10 Diagram".

Let's begin today as we have each day, on our knees…

PRAY.

WRITE. Write Romans 4:20-25* in the lines below. This passage is a good cross reference to Chapter 1. If you have memorized it, write out the passage and then check it!

_____

_____

_____

_____

_____

READ. Open back to the well-worn pages of 2 Timothy Chapter 1 and read the chapter.

INVESTIGATIVE STUDY
REVIEW

Fill in the blank Day 10 Diagrams on the next page by memory or looking at Chapter 1 in your Bible. Afterward, look back at your Day 10 Diagram from Week 3, Day 5 for 2 Timothy.

APPLY!

Take a moment to answers the Apply! questions below.

How has this chapter helped you in living your life?

_____

How has the Lord changed you because of this chapter?

_____

What was the most interesting characteristic about God that you learned in this chapter?

_____

A.C.T.S. PRAYER TIME

Review your prayers from Weeks 2 and 3. Look at all the Lord has done since you began! Go to the Lord in prayer as you close your time with the Lord. Remember, He is not listening to you because you follow four A.C.T.S. steps; He is listening to you because He loves you!

A - *Adoration*_____

C - *Confession*_____

T - *Thanksgiving*_____

S - *Supplication*_____

"There's no better book with which to defend the Bible than the Bible itself."
~D.L. Moody~

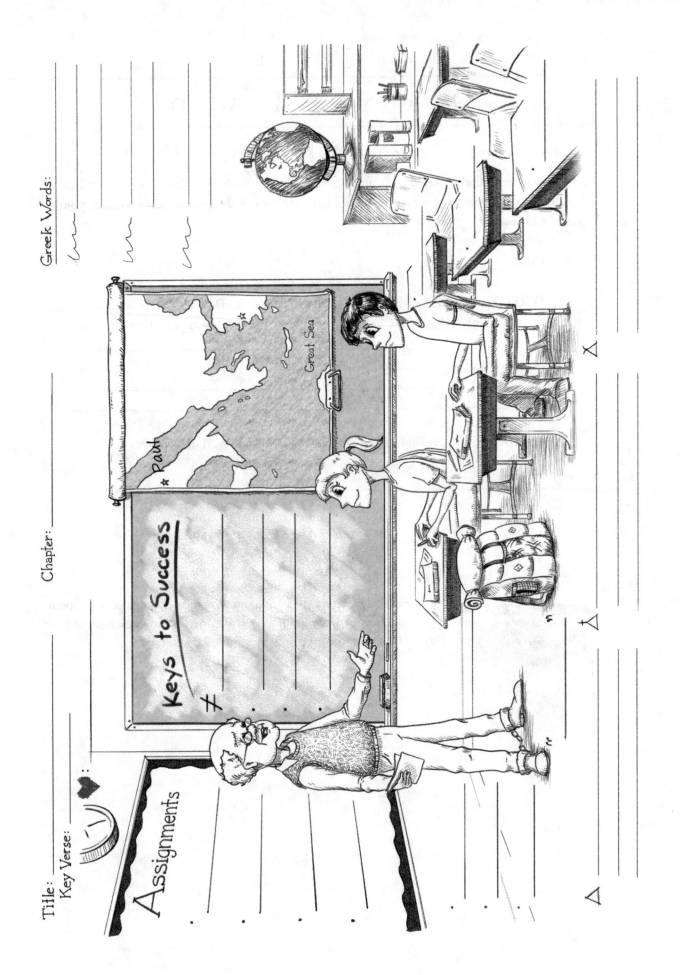

211

DAY TWO

ON MY KNEES:

You are rounding the corner and heading for the finish line! Today, we will review Chapter 2 of 2 Timothy. Do you remember the examples of three hard workers? Start your time in review with prayer.

PRAY.

WRITE. Write Ezekiel 36:23-27* in the lines below. This passage is a good cross reference to Chapter 2. If you have memorized it, write out the passage and then check it!

_____

_____

_____

_____

READ. Turn in your Bible to 2 Timothy, Chapter 2 and read the chapter.

INVESTIGATIVE STUDY
REVIEW

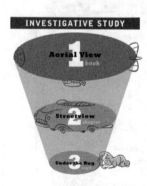

Apply!

Fill in the blank Day 10 Diagrams on the next page page by memory or looking at Chapter 2 in your Bible. Afterward, look back at your Day 10 Diagram from Week 5, Day 5 for 2 Timothy.

APPLY!

Take a moment to answers the Apply! questions below.

How has this chapter helped you in living your life? _____

_____

_____

How has the Lord changed you because of this chapter? _____

_____

What was the most interesting characteristic about God that you learned in this chapter?

_____

A.C.T.S. PRAYER TIME

Where were you as you studied Weeks 4 and 5 of 2 Timothy? Turn back to your prayers on those pages and see all that the Lord has taught you through His Word. Rejoice in His goodness and faithfulness to you through His words.

A - *Adoration* _____

C - *Confession* _____

T - *Thanksgiving* _____

S - *Supplication* _____

*"How often do we really live as Christ? How often do we lay our
own dreams and wants down for God? At church camp? On mission trips?
Maybe even every Sunday or Wednesday? But Christ says DAILY.
Too often do we attempt the whole "Christian living" on Sundays and Wednesdays, and forget
the whole "DAILY Christian dying." Christ calls us to die daily.*
~BJ Higgins~

Title: _____
Key Verse: _____
    : _____

Chapter: _____

Greek Words:
  ⌐ _____
  ⌐ _____

SUFFER HARDSHIP LIKE...

RULES

IF _____ = _____
THEN _____ = _____
    _____ = _____

DAY THREE

ON MY KNEES:

As we hover at this AERIAL VIEW, Chapter 3 of 2 Timothy has come into our view. Before we begin our review, let's go to the Lord in prayer to ask for His additional insights and memories of what we have learned from Paul in this chapter.

PRAY.

WRITE. Write Ephesians 4:11-13* in the lines below. This passage is a good cross reference to Chapter 3. If you have memorized it, write out the passage and then check it!

_____

_____

_____

_____

_____

READ.
Turn in your Bible to 2 Timothy, Chapter 2 and read the chapter.

INVESTIGATIVE STUDY
REVIEW

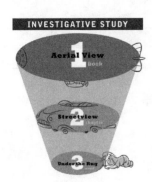

INVESTIGATIVE STUDY

1 Aerial View book

2 Streetview chapter

3 Under the Rug

Apply!

Fill in the blank Day 10 Diagrams on the next page by memory or looking at Chapter 3 in your Bible. Afterward, look back at your Day 10 Diagram from Week 7, Day 5 for 2 Timothy.

APPLY!

Take a moment to answers the Apply! questions below.

How has this chapter helped you in living your life?

_____

How has the Lord changed you because of this chapter?

_____

What was the most interesting characteristic about God that you learned in this chapter?

_____

A.C.T.S. PRAYER TIME

Take this time to pray about how you are living for Jesus. Ask Him for help as you think of the Men of God. Pray for those around you that seem to be thinking more about themselves than about God.

A - *Adoration*_____

C - *Confession*_____

T - *Thanksgiving*_____

S - *Supplication*_____

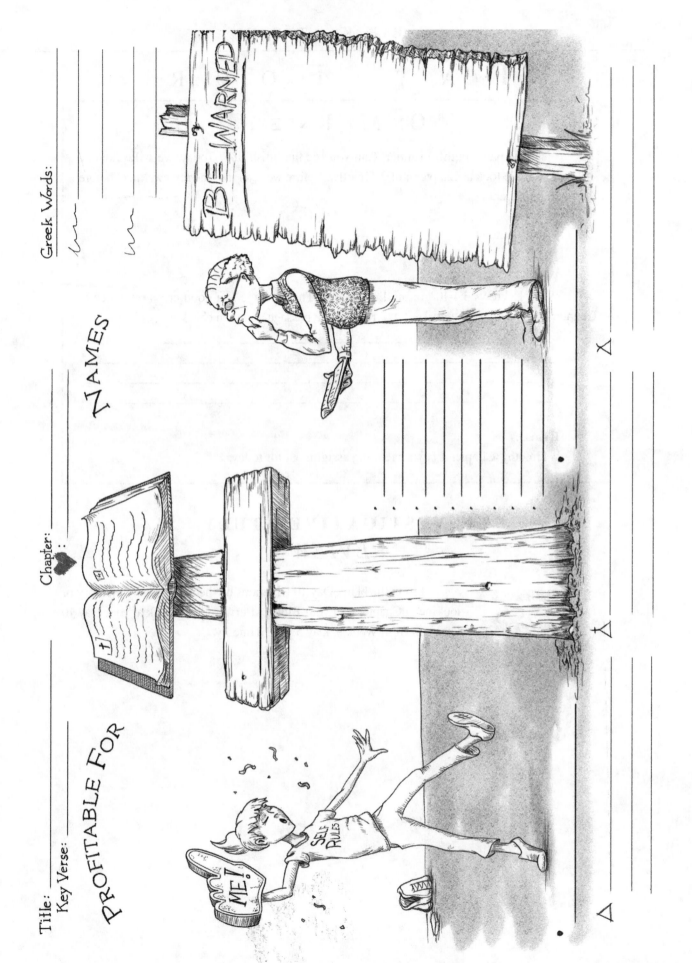

Title: _____

Key Verse: _____

PROFITABLE FOR

Chapter: _____:_____

NAMES

Greek Words:

~ _____

~ _____

BE WARNED

SELF RULES

ME!

217

DAY FOUR

ON MY KNEES:

Welcome back, faithful runner! Can you see the finish line? Today, we will take one last high altitude look at Chapter 4 of 2 Timothy. Before we rush into the review, kneel before the Lord in prayer.

PRAY.

WRITE.

Write Hebrews 3:4-10* in the lines below. This passage is a good cross reference to Chapter 4. If you have memorized it, write out the passage and then check it! _____

_____

_____

_____

_____

READ.

2 Timothy, Chapter 4 is your reading assignment for today.

INVESTIGATIVE STUDY
REVIEW

Apply!

Fill in the blank Day 10 Diagrams on the next page by memory or looking at Chapter 4 in your Bible. Afterward, look back at your Day 10 Diagram from Week 9, Day 5 for 2 Timothy.

APPLY!

Take a moment to answers the Apply! questions below.

How has this chapter helped you in living your life?

_____

How has the Lord changed you because of this chapter?

_____

What was the most interesting characteristic about God that you learned in this chapter?

_____

_____

A.C.T.S. PRAYER TIME

Finish your time with the Lord in prayer. Remember what you learned in Chapter 4 as you ask Jesus for strength to live for Him today and in your future.

A - *Adoration* _____

C - *Confession* _____

T - *Thanksgiving* _____

S - *Supplication* _____

"A centipede was happy till one day, a toad in fun said,
'Pray, which leg goes after which?' Which strained his mind to such a pitch he lay
distracted in a ditch, considering how to run. I think there are a good many
toads in the world, and sometimes, not in fun at all but very seriously, they manage "to strain our
minds to such a pitch", that instead of going on in simplicity we may easily find ourselves distract-
ed in a ditch, not running, but only considering how to run."
~Amy Carmichael~

Greek Words:

Title:

Key Verse:

Chapter:

220

DAY FIVE

ON MY KNEES:

Put your arms up high in the air! Make a joyful noise to the Lord! Rejoice with the Lord in prayer as you begin your final day of your Sword Study of 2 Timothy!

PRAY.

WRITE. Finish your Bible study as you began it 10 weeks ago by writing 2 Timothy 3:16 and 17 on the lines below. If you have memorized it, write out the passage and then check it!

_____

_____

_____

_____

_____

READ. Can you guess what we are going to ask you to do? Please read Paul's letter to Timothy from start to finish.

INVESTIGATIVE STUDY
REVIEW

Apply!

Using the blank Day 10 Diagram on the next page, create your own diagram of the book of 2 Timothy.

APPLY!

Take a moment to answers the Apply! questions below.

Look up 2 Timothy 1:2-7* and what these words mean to you today.

_____
_____
_____
_____

What was the overall lesson of 2 Timothy in your life?

_____
_____
_____
_____

How has the Lord changed you because of your study of 2 Timothy?

_____
_____
_____
_____

What attribute of God have you seen most in this book?

_____
_____
_____
_____

A.C.T.S. PRAYER TIME

The joy of the Lord is our strength, indeed! Write in your prayer starters by considering all that the Lord has taught you through your study of 2 Timothy.

A - *Adoration*_____

C - *Confession*_____

T - *Thanksgiving*_____

S - *Supplication*_____

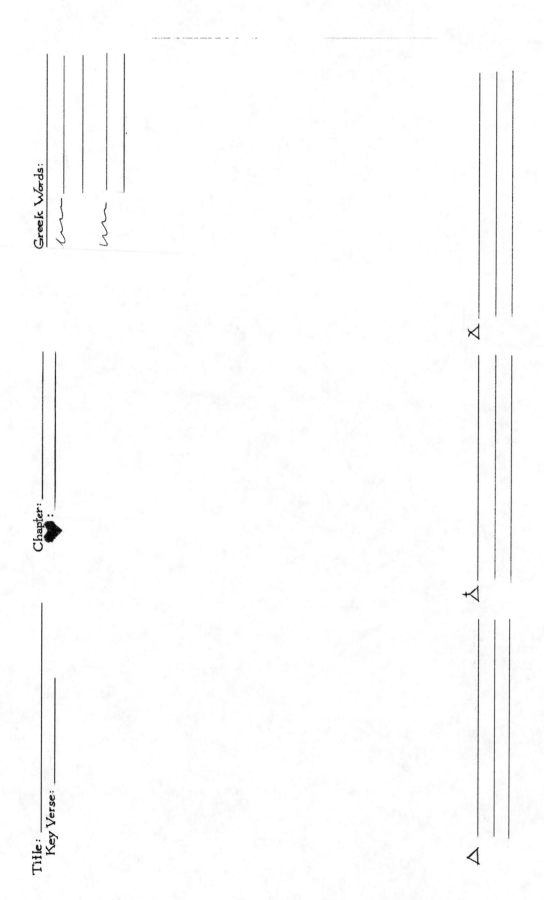

CONGRATULATIONS!

Our prayer for you is that you would …

"Have a salvation for the day of the Lord
Stand Firm in your suffering!
Focus on your inheritance.
Live righteously.
Be Sanctified!
Be aware of the enemy.
Greet one another in His love.
May the peace of Christ be with you until we meet."

You are at the finish line of this race! Well done!

Many times in life the end of one thing is the beginning of another.
We hope that will be true here. You have finished this study of 2 Timothy,
but we hope that you will never finish studying the Bible.
The end of this study can be the beginning of the adventure of studying your
Bible for the rest of your life!

What book will you pick next?

SENIOR SWORD STUDY END NOTES

1. "Euaggelizon." "The KJV New Testament Greek Lexicon." <u>Bible Study Tools</u>. Web. 20 Feb 2012. www.biblestudytools.com/lexicons/greek/kjv/philostorgos.html.

2. "Soldier." "1913 Webster's Dictionary." <u>Hyper Dictionary</u>. Web. 20 Mar 2012. http://www.hyperdictionary.com.

3. "Athlete." "1913 Webster's Dictionary." <u>Hyper Dictionary</u>. Web. 20 Mar 2012. http://www.hyperdictionary.com.

4. "Farmer." "1913 Webster's Dictionary." <u>Hyper Dictionary</u>. Web. 20 Mar 2012. http://www.hyperdictionary.com.

5. MacArthur, John. <u>The MacArthur New Testament Commentary 2 Timothy</u>. Chicago: Moody Publishers, 1995.

6. Chambers, Oswald. <u>My Utmost for His Highest</u>. Special Updated Edition. Ed. James Reimann. Grand Rapids: Discovery House Publishers in affiliation with RBC Ministries, 1995.

7. Langham, Andrew. "Comments on the Drink Offering." <u>Biblecentre.org</u>. Web. 20 Mar. 2012. http://www.biblecentre.org/topics/al_drink_offering.htm

WRITE!
MY COPY OF 2 TIMOTHY

GOD
the Father

GOD
the Son

GOD
the Holy Spirit

GOD
the Father

GOD
the Son

GOD
the Holy Spirit

GOD
the Father

GOD
the Son

GOD
the Holy Spirit

GOD
the Father

GOD
the Son

GOD
the Holy Spirit

GOD
the Father

GOD
the Son

GOD
the Holy Spirit

GOD
the Father

GOD
the Son

GOD
the Holy Spirit

GOD
the Father

GOD
the Son

GOD
the Holy Spirit

GOD
the Father

GOD
the Son

GOD
the Holy Spirit

GOD
the Father

GOD
the Son

GOD
the Holy Spirit

STUDY TOOLS

For Going Deeper

The following is a list of suggested resources to aid you in your study of God's Word. We hope you find the format and information helpful and easy to use. The notes below individual resources (if any) are given to help students and parents choose the resources best suited to their ability, experience, and age.

General Reference

Logos Bible Software. An excellent resource for the entire family to encourage life long investigation of Gods word.

BibleGateway.com

Holman Illustrated Bible Dictionary. Edited by Charles W. Draper, Chad Brand, and Archie England. Broadman & Holman Publishing, 2003.

The International Standard Bible Encyclopedia. Four Volumes. Edited by Geoffrey W. Bromiley. William B. Eerdmans Publishing Co., 1995.

Leland Ryken, Philip Ryken, and James Wilhoit. Ryken's Bible Handbook: *A Guide to Reading and Studying the Bible. Tyndale House Publishers, 2005.*

James Strong. *The New Strong's Exhaustive Concordance of the Bible.* Thomas Nelson Publishers, 2010.

Word Studies

The Complete Word Study Dictionary: New Testament. Word Study Series. Edited by Spiros Zodhiates. AMG Publishers, 1992.

> A helpful resource for beginning students and beyond. Can be used with Strong's Exhaustive Concordance of the Bible or with The Complete Word Study New Testament with Greek Parallel both listed below.

The Complete Word Study New Testament with Greek Parallel: Bringing the Original Text to Life. Word Study Series. Edited by Spiros Zodhiates. AMG Publishers, 1992.

> A helpful resource for beginning students and beyond. This resource has the complete text of the New Testament and the corresponding Strong's number above the text. The Bible version is the KJV, so the student will use the Greek Word provided in the curriculum and then refer to it in the reference book. The definitions are listed by number in the corresponding resource The Complete Word Study Dictionary: New Testament listed above.

New International Dictionary of New Testament Theology. Four Volumes. Edited by Colin Brown. Zondervan Publishing House, 1986.

> An excellent resource for more advanced students.

New International Dictionary of Old Testament Theology and Exegesis. Five Volumes. Edited by Willem A. VanGemeren. Zondervan Publishing House, 1997.

The New Linguistic and Exegetical Key to the Greek New Testament. Edited by Cleon L. Rogers, Jr. and Cleon L. Rogers III. Zondervan Publishing House, 1998.

Vincent's Word Studies in the New Testament. Four Volumes. Edited by Marvin R. Vincent. Hendrickson Publishers, 1985.

Word Studies in the Greek New Testament. Four Volumes. Edited by Kenneth S. Wuest. William B. Eerdmans Publishing Co., 2002.

Additional Resources

MacKenzie, Catherine. Amy Carmichael: Can Brown Eyes Be Made Blue? Scotland, UK: Christian Focus Publications, 2005.
MacKenzie, Catherine. Corrie Ten Boom: Are All of the Watches Safe? Scotland, UK: Christian Focus Publications, 2005.
MacKenzie, Catherine. George Muller: Does Money Grow on Trees? Scotland, UK: Christian Focus Publications, 2005.
MacKenzie, Catherine. David Livingstone: Who is the Bravest? Scotland, UK: Christian Focus Publications, 2005.
MacKenzie, Catherine. John Calvin: What is the Truth? Scotland, UK: Christian Focus Publications, 2005.
MacKenzie, Catherine. Martin Luther: What Should I Do? Scotland, UK: Christian Focus Publications, 2005.
Howat, Irene. Ten Boys who Changed the World. Scotland, Great Britain: Christian Focus Publications, 2003.
Howat, Irene. Ten Boys who Didn't Give In. Scotland, Great Britain: Christian Focus Publications, 2004.
Howat, Irene. Ten Boys who Made a Difference. Scotland, Great Britain: Christian Focus Publications, 2002.
Howat, Irene. Ten Boys who Made History. Scotland, Great Britain: Christian Focus Publications, 2003.
Howat, Irene. Ten Boys who Used Their Talents. Scotland, Great Britain: Christian Focus Publications, 2006.
Howat, Irene. Ten Girls who Changed the World. Scotland, Great Britain: Christian Focus Publications, 2001.
Howat, Irene. Ten Girls who Didn't Give In. Scotland, Great Britain: Christian Focus Publications, 2003.
Howat, Irene. Ten Girls who Made a Difference. Scotland, Great Britain: Christian Focus Publications, 2002.
Howat, Irene. Ten Girls who Made History. Scotland, Great Britain: Christian Focus Publications, 2003.
Howat, Irene. Ten Girls who Used Their Talents. Scotland, Great Britain: Christian Focus Publications, 2006.
William Tyndale Story. Torchlighters, DVD. Visionvideo.com.
Perpetua Story. Torchlighters, DVD. Visionvideo.com.
William Tyndale Story. Torchlighters, DVD. Visionvideo.com.
Jim Elliot Story. Torchlighters, DVD. Visionvideo.com.
Amy Carmichael Story. Torchlighters, DVD. Visionvideo.com.
Gladys Aylward Story. Torchlighters, DVD. Visionvideo.com.
John Bunyan Story. Torchlighters, DVD. Visionvideo.com.
Richard Wurmbrand Story. Torchlighters, DVD. Visionvideo.com.
Eric Liddel Story. Torchlighters, DVD. Visionvideo.com.
William Booth Story. Torchlighters, DVD. Visionvideo.com.
Jesus: He Lived Among Us. Voice of the Martys, DVD. Visionvideo.com.
Higgins, Brent and Deanna. I Would Die for You: One Student's Story of Passion, Service, and Faith.